The Business of Invention

The essentials of success for inventors and innovators

Peter Bissell & Graham Barker

abettermousetrap.co.uk

P O Box 65 Hebden Bridge HX7 8WT
www.abettermousetrap.co.uk
mail@abettermousetrap.co.uk

THE BUSINESS OF INVENTION
First published in 1998, revised 2004
by abettermousetrap.co.uk
P O Box 65 Hebden Bridge HX7 8WT
www.abettermousetrap.co.uk

ISBN 0 951 3856 31

Printed in Great Britain
by Printout
Dean Clough Halifax HX3 5AX

By the same authors:
A BETTER MOUSETRAP: A GUIDE FOR INNOVATORS

Unauthorized and illegal copying

Don't do it. We understand that desperation, deadlines, the handout dependency of a baying audience etc sometimes drive otherwise law-abiding people to the photocopier, but when it happens it's surprising how often someone recognizes the stuff and tells us. We are however always happy to consider requests to reproduce acknowledged extracts as long as we know why, when, where, which bits and so on.

The Chartered Institute of Patent Agents

The views and advice expressed in this book are those of the authors and not of the Chartered Institute of Patent Agents, which is pleased to endorse the book as a general introduction to protecting and exploiting intellectual property for private inventors. Legal and financial issues discussed in the book are complex and advice from professionally qualified advisors should be sought.

Contents

Acknowledgements

We would like to offer our lasting gratitude (rather than something more fleeting, like money) to everyone who in one way or another helped bring this book to fruition. We must in particular thank:

Government Office (formerly DTI) Yorkshire & Humberside, whose financial support in 1988 made possible everything thereafter.

Hilary Trudeau, formerly BP Innovations Adviser, without whose championing of our first book there might not have been a second edition, let alone a second title.

The Committee and Council of The Chartered Institute of Patent Agents, for suggesting improvements to the text and for bestowing their official approval on the book.

Bob Pidgeon of Appleyard Lees and John Williams of Williams, Powell & Associates, for guidance on aspects of intellectual property protection.

Don Wilkinson of Exsell Technical Communications, for guidance on the section on free publicity.

Ken Wade, for his entrepreneurial and business advice.

Jayne Bissell, for exceptional fortitude when chasing up entries for the Useful Addresses section.

Jeremy Burgoyne and colleagues at the Department of Trade & Industry, for encouragement, advice and information.

Peter Robson of Leeds Patent Unit, for his advice and work on patent searching.

Preface

This book is a distillation of some of the things we've learned about turning inventions into commercial products since we ran a local authority innovation centre in the early 1980s. Back then, hardly anyone - including us - seemed to know what you actually had to *do* when you'd invented something. At first our centre just made prototypes for local inventors, on the grounds that this was all the help they needed; but as enquiries flooded in from all over the UK (and even from the USA), we soon realized that the real need was for a far wider range of advice and support.

The innovation centre couldn't take the strain. It made no money and created so much nervousness and suspicion when it spent any that a brief existence was always on the cards. Yet in its increasingly bumpy seven years it managed to advise and help going on for 1500 inventors and small businesses, despite an advertising budget that stretched to no more than 2000 leaflets. Since then, one of us has become even more immersed in innovation; the other took an easier way out and merely writes about it.

Perhaps our most surprising discovery in those years was that no one seemed ever to have written a guide to invention. By then we were spending two or three hours per inventor going through the basic 'do this, don't do that' stuff and were desperate for something we could hand out and say: 'Read this first, *then* come and talk to us'. So we wrote our own guide, which evolved into a short, self-published book called A Better Mousetrap: a Guide for Inventors. Like many new products it initially hung around selling in dribs and drabs. That changed dramatically when it was adopted by BP for its Support for Innovation network, now also defunct.

Eight years and four editions later (five if you include a 'special' for The Open University), A Better Mousetrap has generated a great deal of positive feedback from inventors, small firms and others who have used it. That feedback is incorporated in The Business of Invention.

As its title suggests, The Business of Invention looks beyond the invention to *the business opportunity*; it is essentially a book about developing a new product that just *happens* to be an invention. It also looks beyond the inventor to *the entrepreneur.* This reflects the fact that there is now far more help available - and by extension, a better chance of success - for a small business based on a new product than for a private inventor. Yet with relatively little effort or expense or risk, that small business and that inventor can be one and the same person. We reveal all, as they say.

And although for the average inventor a royalty agreement with a company is still the best option, the 'average inventor' is changing. As one highly successful inventor/entrepreneur told us: 'Because of redundancy, early retirement, part-time working and all the rest you've now got large numbers of experienced professional problem-solvers on the loose out there, with a head full of product and marketing ideas and the time and motivation to develop them into some kind of enterprise. All they need is a bit of pointing in the right direction and they can do it'. This book is a bit of pointing in the right direction. And we hope you *can* do it.

Finally: the following chapters owe much to inventors who told us about their experiences, and to others - patent agents, business and technical advisers, companies, even the odd millionaire - who gave us further valuable insights. Please let us know how *you* get on, especially if you think parts of this book need improving or changing as a result, because this edition is not the last word on anything. Our aim is to develop The Business of Invention over the years as a primary source of guidance and information for inventors, innovative small businesses, and all those who help them.

Graham Barker
Peter Bissell
May 1998

A familiar ring?

Flushed with excitement, Bell and Watson demonstrated their new device to Western Union, but the company's executives failed to see its potential. 'Mr Bell,' they wrote to him, 'after careful consideration of your invention, while it is a very interesting novelty, we have come to the conclusion that it has no commercial possibilities,' adding that they saw no future for 'an electrical toy'. Fortunately for Bell, others were not so short-sighted. Within just four years of its invention, America had 60,000 telephones. In the next twenty years that figure would increase to over six million, and Bell's telephone company, renamed American Telephone and Telegraph, would become the largest corporation in America, with stock worth $1,000 a share. The Bell patent (No.174,465) became the single most valuable patent in history. The speed with which the telephone insinuated itself into American life is indicated by the fact that by the early 1880s when a person said 'I'll call you' it was taken to mean by telephone - or phone, as it was already familiarly known.

Introduction

You've invented something

Or think you have. And you want to make a fortune out of it. You have four basic options:

❶ To sell your idea outright.

❷ To license your idea to a company in return for a royalty agreement.

❸ To manufacture and market the product yourself.

❹ To develop and market the product as a joint venture with another company.

This book gives you detailed advice on them all. But first it tells you:

- How to assess your idea's originality and market prospects.
- How to develop and present your idea for serious consideration by others.
- How to protect your intellectual property.
- How to make key decisions about commercial exploitation.
- Where to get the right kind of help.
- What - and who - to avoid.
- How to keep your personal risk and costs to a minimum.

Throughout the book we also try to give a parallel view of inventors, invention and innovation as seen from the business and professional world. That includes company managers, business advisers, financial backers, patent agents (or patent attorneys internationally), designers etc. It's vital to understand how these people think because it is their opinions and actions rather than the merits of your idea which will win or lose the day for you.

The chapters follow on in logical sequence, but in practice you'll find yourself having to handle several strands at the same time. Read the book through, then work out an action plan to suit your idea and your circumstances. Once your project is under way, use the Checklist at the back to help you monitor progress.

Where do inventors go wrong?

Statistically, most inventions fail. Only one in 100 more than covers its costs, only one in 300 makes a significant difference to a company and only one in 1400 is a world beater. The reality however is that most failures are either inevitable because the idea is flawed, or made inevitable by the inventor's mishandling of some aspect of development. Inventors who focus primarily on avoiding mistakes have a much better time of it - and that's what this book is all about.

The overwhelming majority of inventions fail right at the start, either because they're not original - and thus can't even be called inventions - or because the market they're aimed at doesn't want them. *This probably accounts for around 90 per cent of inventors' ideas.* The further you develop an idea without first doing a patent and product search (Chapter 1) and enough market research to establish a potential market (Chapter 2), the deeper is the hole you're digging for yourself.

The next common cause of failure is the invention that is good, but not the best solution to the problem it addresses. Inventors must analyse problems fully and not assume they've got it right first time. An idea may be technically brilliant but too complex for most people to use, or require too radical a change in their behaviour, or be too expensive. One lesson of markets is that something less good may make a more successful product.

Many genuinely promising ideas are abandoned when the innovator's money runs out. In the case of lone inventors this typically happens when so much is spent on one aspect, for example patenting, that nothing is left for other priorities such as a prototype. The lesson is not so much that you need more money - though that is useful - but rather that you spend it wisely.

Good ideas which have been skilfully developed can 'fail' when companies first accept, then reject them; but if your confidence in your idea is high, a solution may lie in taking another route to market and starting your own business venture (Chapters 13-18).

Other causes of failure or uphill struggle lie squarely with the inventor. Some present their ideas too early, with basic technical flaws glaringly apparent. Some have an over-inflated belief in their own expertise. Some are a pushover for rip-off merchants and dodgy associates (Chapter 5). Some don't understand the requirements of companies and do little to present their ideas professionally (Chapter 9). Many try to sell their ideas to the wrong companies (Chapter 8).

Even when a decent deal is on the table, inventors can find ways to blow it. Some are pathologically greedy, upping their price every time agreement is near. Some insist on impossible conditions (usually the right to meddle or veto). Some are so obsessed with their 'baby' that they can't let go. The only thing that stops companies kicking them through the door is the profit potential of the idea, or the thought of losing development money already spent - but people are human and even that won't restrain them forever.

Finally, a tiny minority of inventors come from a different planet where they're presumably not regarded as pests. There are paranoiacs plagued by burglars who steal nothing but their blueprints; there are egotistic bores who write to the Prime Minister when ignored. There is the originator of a low-energy furnace who proudly showed us photos of how well it had incinerated a very large dead dog, insisting that all he needed to perfect it was 'a hydraulic'. These people have some entertainment value, but it is they who make it difficult to call yourself an inventor and be taken seriously.

The inevitable risk

If innovation is such a universally good thing, why do inventors have a hard time getting their ideas accepted? The answer is that innovation = uncertainty = risk, and that applies to all companies irrespective of size. Most prefer to focus on the *continuous improvement* of their existing successful products, making changes here and there to raise quality, cut costs, supply customers more quickly, open up new markets etc. Those which innovate tend to do it cautiously, rearranging existing components or modifying an existing design to produce something that performs a new or additional task. This may be unadventurous but all the elements are familiar, enabling the company to predict and control most of its risk.

Inventions on the other hand involve unfamiliar elements, one of which is the inventor himself or herself. The risk is immediately larger and less calculable, and for that reason will often be unacceptable. Small companies may fear the cost; large companies may fear a drop in share price if investors see them dabbling in untried products or unfamiliar markets.

None the less, there is plenty of room for inventions. If they're to stand a chance of competing, many companies have to risk the occasional bold leap that inventions represent and that the safer innovation-by-evolution process tends not to produce. If yours is the right idea presented in the right way to the right company or market *and you avoid mistakes*, you stand a good chance of success.

Controlling your costs

We assume you're not rich, and one of our main aims is to minimize your cost and risk. You should be able to reach the first critical stage - is your idea original and saleable? - for around £200; less if you do everything yourself. If you go beyond that point, some significant expenditure is unavoidable. It's impossible to give exact figures, but you should think in terms of spending something like £1000 on your idea, including fees for *initial* professional advice, for example from a patent agent or designer. The nature of your idea will affect the cost of things like a prototype or redesign, so it's worth using part of that initial budget to buy advice on (a) what later costs you can expect and (b) how you can minimize them.

For an idea that needs patenting (Chapter 6), that notional £1000 won't stretch much beyond the initial filing of your application if you use a patent agent. Twelve months later, official and professional fees will become substantial and unavoidable if you want to go on. In the meantime you'll have to spend money developing and raising interest in your idea. If by the deadline you haven't got a deal that somehow covers patenting costs (either a company pays them or you recover them gradually through royalties or sales), you face a common inventors' dilemma. Do you pay thousands to keep your idea in play, or do you let it go?

Personal expenditure on an invention is not normally tax deductible, and most innovation grants and subsidies are not available to private individuals. You may be in a better position if you operate as a business (Chapters 4 and 13). But however you tackle development and exploitation, *never spend money unless (a) you can afford it or (b) you see a clear prospect of getting it back.* Many good ideas have been lost because developing an invention has turned into servicing a debt.

The golden rule is *never spend more than your idea is likely to be worth to you.* Many inventors have come to grief by ignoring this commonsense safeguard. It's one thing to gamble an affordable sum to at least get an idea out of your system - you may regret it forever if you don't - but another thing altogether to ruin yourself financially by chasing a hopeless dream.

Chapter 1
Is your idea original?

Originality matters

An idea can't really be called an invention unless it contains some element or combination of elements that is (a) completely original and (b) non-obvious - that is, it wouldn't readily occur to someone skilled in that particular 'art' or technology.

If your idea isn't at least partly original, your options are so limited that in many cases it probably won't be worth carrying on. Why not?

- Few if any companies will be interested in acquiring a licence to make or sell your idea, so you can't look forward to any royalties.
- If you do manage to get a licence deal and it then emerges that your idea isn't original, you'll not only lose the licence but may also be sued by the licensee.
- 'Your' idea may legally belong to someone else. Infringe their intellectual property and they too could sue you.

Making and selling the product yourself might be an option if there's no danger of infringement, but marketing a product based on an unprotectable idea is always risky and you'd almost certainly have trouble getting financial backing.

You can't simply assume that your idea is original because you don't know of anything like it – a mistake many inventors make. You must either spend some money or put in some hard graft to find out what original elements your idea *might* contain. (The 'might' is essential. As you'll soon discover, originality is not a black-and-white matter; there are acres of grey.)

If you find out early on that your idea isn't original, no harm is done. You might even be able to improve it so that it is original. But if you don't bother to find out and carry on regardless - as far too many inventors do - you could easily land yourself in serious financial and legal trouble. Consequences can include costly patent applications and prototypes, total loss of credibility, and legal action by an aggrieved licensee or intellectual property owner.

(Cautionary example 1: the inventor of a special spanner system spent £30,000 on foreign patent applications without first carrying out a world patent search for a fraction of the cost. Once official searches began – see Chapter 6 – similar existing patents emerged in abundance and he was left with nothing protectable. Cautionary example 2: the inventor of an apparatus to whisk away toilet bowl odours kitted himself out with a complete working toilet which he carted around in his car, laying on many hundreds of demonstration flushes before finding an interested company. Unfortunately he hadn't done a patent search because nobody told him he should. The company did its own search and found so many similar patents that again the inventor was left with nothing worth protecting. The deal collapsed and the inventor threw away his toilet.)

Prior art

You must search for **prior art**, a legal term that means anything already known and recorded that is close enough to your idea to enable someone to say 'It – or that bit of it - has been done before'. Prior art embraces all media and every period of history and includes every unworkable and pointless idea that has ever been recorded anywhere in the world, so it's possible that your idea for a mobile phone accessory could be deemed non-original because something like it was drawn in a 1930s science fiction comic.

It's important to be thorough in your search, because the more prior art there is relating to your idea, the slimmer will be your chances of claiming a significant degree of originality.

To find out how original your idea might be you should carry out two searches **before you do anything else**, and certainly before you spend any serious money on your idea. And **do both searches**. One isn't a substitute for the other.

Disclosure

Before you start looking for prior art, beware of disclosures to other people. Strictly speaking, any disclosure of your invention that isn't in confidence could prevent it from being patented later. On the other hand you have to tell people something or you'll get nowhere. In general, revealing what your invention does may be safe; revealing how it does it is dangerous. Never show drawings or detailed specifications except in conditions of documented confidentiality (Chapter 6) or to someone like a patent attorney who observes confidentiality as a matter of course.

Don't on the other hand be dramatically secretive; the common fear that someone will steal your idea is usually groundless. Take sensible precautions when dealing with experts who may only need a couple of clues to work out what you've got, but the blunt truth is that most people will probably be totally unmoved by your idea. Always remember that a company will be much more interested in what it can do for their profits than in the technology.

Product search

You need to find out what's already on the market that is (a) similar to your idea and (b) tackles the same problem.

It's obvious why you should look for products with a similar form and function, but why look for products that are different? The reason is that most inventions are a solution to a problem and there's nearly always more than one way of solving that problem. Before you can make any kind of judgment about the commercial potential of your idea, you need to know about **all** the competition it might face. In this respect originality searching overlaps with market research, which we'll deal with later.

The easiest way to look for product information is to use a search engine. If you're stuck for search terms, go looking for specialist words used 'in the trade'. For example, a search we once did on sending personal health data via the internet found very little until we came across a news report that used the terms e-health, e-care, e-monitoring and telemedicine. Using them as keywords we soon found what we were looking for.

For as long as you stay with your idea you should never stop looking at existing products. As well as internet searching look around retail and trade outlets, get hold of product lists and catalogues, look through specialist journals, and pick the brains of people who are likely to know. To get information without disclosing your idea, simply ask how people deal at present with the problem your idea aims to solve.

Patent search

A patent search uncovers ideas from other countries as well

as ideas which never (or haven't yet) made it as products, so it will be a much more thorough guide to prior art than a product search. Points to bear in mind are:

- Even an official Patent Office search can't prove originality beyond doubt or dispute.
- Patents only cover what is patentable; but what is not patentable can still be prior art.
- Any patent, no matter how old or absurd, is prior art.
- Foreign patents are prior art and must be searched.
- Absence of prior art does not automatically mean you should patent your idea.

Patents and patenting are dealt with more fully in Chapter 6.

When it comes to patent search costs, you have four ascending options:

- Do it yourself online by using the free and excellent Espacenet patent database (see below).
- Do it largely yourself but with the help of a patent or reference library. Many will carry out a brief online search for a usually modest fee.
- Use the Patent Office's Search and Advisory Service (www.patent.gov.uk/patent/sas/index.htm or phone 01633 811010). Options and costs vary.
- Use a patent attorney, but discuss fees first as they vary according to the type of search you need.

Cost shouldn't however be the sole factor. Selecting the right area to search isn't always easy, and the real skill in patent searching lies in interpreting the findings. All this may be difficult for a novice. A patent attorney's search and assessment will cost more initially, but could be better value in the long run.

How to do your own Espacenet search

By far the easiest way to search and view worldwide patents

is to use Espacenet, the European Patent Office database. What follows is only a very unofficial 'get you started' guide. For more detail – particularly on how to use Boolean operators and other nifty search stuff - we strongly recommend the excellent Espacenet manual, downloadable from www.european-patent-office.org/espacenet/info/manual.htm.

Let's first summarize what you're going to do.

- You'll use simple **keyword searches** to find at least some relevant patents, then sift through them one by one. This may be all you need to do.
- Preferably though, you'll use some of the patents you've found as a stepping-stone to the relevant **EC classification(s)** for your idea. These list patents by subject and can give better results than keywords alone.
- You'll retrieve all patents in each relevant EC classification. This gives you a siftable 'hit list' of all patents in the same technology area as your idea.

How long will all this take? It's impossible to say. It can range from minutes if there's obvious killer prior art, to many hours if there are hundreds of patents to examine and only a slowly emerging prior art picture.

Finding your 'hit list' of potentially relevant patents

List all combinations of up to four keywords that best capture the essence of your idea. Include synonyms (for example baby, child, infant) and different spellings and terminologies (for example tyre/tire, nappy/diaper, car/automobile). To find plurals and other variants - for example ventilator(s), ventilate(s), ventilated, ventilating, ventilation - key in 'ventilat*' and Espacenet finds every word longer than 'ventilat'. Then:

❶ Go to **http://gb.espacenet.com**. The Quick Search page opens immediately.

❷ Enter your keyword(s) in the 'Simple Text' field. Click 'Search' and in a few seconds get:

❸ A results list. The titles should tell you whether you're in the right neck of the woods. If not, try a different search string. Scan the titles, disregarding any that clearly aren't relevant.

❹ Look at patents that sound relevant by clicking on the patent number. This first opens up a reference or summary screen, which usually includes an Abstract. This may be all you need to decide that the patent isn't relevant, in which case go back to your titles list and try another likely-looking patent.

❺ If you can't tell whether it's relevant (some Abstracts are as clear as mud), open up the patent itself by clicking the number in blue on the line 'Patent number' or 'Requested patent'. Look at the drawing. Does it bear similarities to your idea?

After a few goes at this you may have found enough prior art to stop searching. If you do need to carry on, try this:

❻ Once you've found a relevant patent, go back to its reference screen and look for the EC classification number in blue. Click on it. (There may be more than one.)

❼ A pop-up screen appears, highlighting that EC classification. Study its description carefully. Does it sound like the right one for your idea?

8. Get a full list of all patents in that classification by checking the box alongside the classification and clicking Search at the bottom of the screen.

9. Repeat 6-8 with a few other patents to make sure you're finding the most relevant classification(s).

10. If you end up with very long lists, try adding keywords to refine your search. Go to the Advanced Search screen (click the binocular icon if visible, or go to the Simple Search screen and click on the line in red that says 'Worldwide – 30 million documents'). Once there, fill in the 'EC Classification' and 'Title or Abstract' fields.

Examining individual patents

11. To open any patent on your hit list, click its number. Read the Abstract and/or open the patent. Look especially at any drawings. If what you find clearly isn't close to your idea, you're done with that patent and can move on to another on your list.

A problem from now on is that patent pages open only singly so you can't open, print or download the whole patent in one go. (We trust you're keeping records of your findings as you go along.) To save time, the knack is to look at key pieces of information and avoid having to read or store the entire patent, which may not be in English anyway. Those key pieces of information are accessed by the buttons at the top of the screen and are:

12. The **Drawings**. The full set may reveal more than the single example on the front page. Treat drawings with caution though, as Claims (see below) matter more.

⑬ The **Search Report** (**SR** button) or list of **References Cited** on the patent front page. Both can be extremely useful as they list other patents – sometimes very different - that an examiner has regarded as prior or relevant art. (See **Widen your search** below.)

⑭ If a patent looks relevant but you're not sure how relevant, look at the **Claims** - the breakdown of the idea into all its alleged inventive steps. Claims can be tricky to interpret but do any of them sound like the claims you'd have to make for your own idea? If they do, the patent may be relevant as you won't be able to claim what has already been granted.

⑮ You should by now have a good enough grasp of the patent to decide whether it's relevant or not. If you still can't decide, you may have to bite the bullet and read it in full.

Widen your search

The beauty of recent patents is that they usually incorporate a search report listing other patents which official examiners have considered relevant and indicating their level of importance and the claims to which they relate. Whenever you find a patent containing something even remotely relevant to your idea, look for this report. If any patent on it is not on your hit list, add it on and look at it. Thanks to an examiner's diligence you may find something crucial hidden away in an unexpected classification. Adding in this way to your original list may also cure weaknesses caused by a flawed description of your idea.

Completing your search

By eliminating numbers from your original list and adding

new ones you pick up along the way, your search becomes steadily more thorough and effective. When you've run out of numbers you can conclude with reasonable confidence that (a) your idea is covered in whole or in part by prior art or (b) it isn't, in which case it may be original.

Assess your findings

Once you've assembled a list of relevant patents, you then have to assess it. If your idea is clearly covered by prior art, abandon any thought of patenting it; you needn't necessarily drop the idea itself, but your development options will be much more limited. If the picture is less clear, only a patent attorney is competent to study your findings and advise on your chances of getting a patent. If he or she can give an opinion in a short time, it's money well spent, especially if the view is that you probably won't get a patent (or at best a very weak one). The sum you then save could be huge.

File a patent application?

If you're confident that you don't need a second opinion, you could file your own patent application at low or no cost. But patenting is a minefield. Read Chapter 6 at least twice and if you can afford it, retain a patent attorney to advise and act for you.

Update your search

What you won't find during your search are relevant applications which haven't yet been published. (In the USA, *nothing* is published until the patent is granted.) If you go ahead with development of your idea it's essential to top up your patent search every few weeks, even after you've filed your own application.

Chapter 2
Assessing demand for your idea

Market research

Originality on its own means nothing. You must now research possible markets for your idea to find out if there is likely to be enough demand to justify you or a company developing it as a product. If the results are not clearly promising, it usually isn't worth carrying on; the risk is too great. Questions you must attempt to answer include:

- **Does anyone actually need your product?**

  Do enough people experience the problem you have identified to warrant a new product dedicated to its solution? Are the limitations of existing products outweighed by other benefits you haven't considered? If they're selling strongly the market may be satisfied with them, and a product that is only slightly better would need to be significantly cheaper to stand a chance. Prospects are brighter if your product offers several clear advantages, but it may still take a lot of effort to break through the 'so what?' barrier. Never underestimate the sticking power of a well-established product.

- **What's the competition?**

  Identify and assess the strengths and weaknesses of all competing products, including totally dissimilar ones if they're currently used to tackle the problem your idea addresses. Habit is also your competition; it may be difficult to persuade people to abandon tried and tested ways of doing things, especially if your idea challenges conventional wisdom. Habit covers not just techniques, but practices such as using a tradesman rather than a DIY product. *Reassess your competition constantly, as new products come along all the time.*

- **What's the best market for your product?**

  This isn't always easy, as markets can range from the entire universe for a consumer product like Coca Cola™ to a mere handful of companies for, say, a rarified piece of industrial test equipment. There also may not be much overlap between apparently similar markets; tailor your product to one and you might shut yourself out of another which is more profitable. For example, you develop a shower fitting as a budget home product when you might have done better with a higher-spec version for the hotel sector. Many products can be developed in different directions and it's often a non-obvious one that pays off, so spend plenty of time digging around for gaps in the market. If your idea is sufficiently flexible there may be a niche somewhere just waiting for it, albeit perhaps in a modified or customised form.

- **What's the easiest market to enter?**

  If you intend to market your own product, this is a crucial factor that we'll return to later. To minimise your risk, making easy sales has to be a priority in the early stages, so if your target market is hard or costly to enter, identify a 'soft' - perhaps local - market to start with *even if it's less profitable.* Experience and a trading record will soon make it easier to crack the tougher nut, and may also favourably influence potential financial backers.

- **How healthy is your selected market?**

  What's the market worth annually and is it moving up or down? You should hesitate to enter a declining market, unless you feel your product can revive it.

Looking into the future, are there any emerging technological, social or other changes that might radically affect its fortunes?

- **At what price and quantity might your product sell profitably?**

  Price isn't everything, but it might as well be. Get your price wrong and you either won't make sales or won't make a profit. You can't command your price; it must fall within the range set by competing products or services, and even if your product is a big improvement it must still be priced at what the market will bear. If that isn't going to be possible, you may have to alter drastically either your product or your marketing plans. Once you've fixed a realistic selling price, try to estimate how many units a year you might sell and what percentage of the market that represents. You need that information (a) to help persuade companies of the value of your idea or (b) as an essential part of your business plan, and (c) to give you some idea of the level of risk that might be justified. *Don't be tempted to overestimate market share. In the early stages even one per cent may be wildly optimistic.*

- **What's the most marketable aspect of your invention?**

  It may turn out that only a portion of your idea is marketable. If this can be incorporated in an existing product or design it may be pointless to proceed with the whole invention. You may discover this now or at the patenting stage, when you're left with fewer worthwhile claims for originality than you'd hoped.

Market research strategy

- You'll probably have to do your own research. Companies won't do it for you and professional market researchers are expensive. They may also miss vital clues or nuances unless they understand your idea as well as you do or you brief them in exhaustive detail.

- Your research could last from a few days if you get negative results to months or years if your project progresses. You must update and expand your market knowledge all the time, for even if all else goes well, poor research can cause serious problems later if there is even a slight mismatch between product and market.

- Don't make the common mistake of talking only to potential *consumers* - or worse, only to trusted friends and relatives, who will lie to you. Consumers can say one thing and do another; it's their privilege. They're not committed to products in the way that retailers, manufacturers and distributors have to be. It is they who gamble huge sums which they may not recover if a product doesn't sell, so their opinion matters far more *when you can safely get it.* (See **To go on or not to go on** at the end of this Chapter.)

- If you feel the need to conduct consumer surveys (see **Danger!** below), get people to focus on how they perceive and deal with the problem your idea addresses rather than on the idea itself. This avoids disclosure and ensures that you're not simply fishing for approval of your idea. It may also reveal other, perhaps better ways of tackling the problem. *If a significant minority don't like your idea, don't ignore them. Find out why, in case they've given the matter more thought than the others and detected a major drawback.*

- Keep competent records of all your research. During the presenting, negotiating or money-raising stages of your project you will need ready access to all your data. And use only primary sources of information. For example, if you want to prove rising levels of school truancy to justify your revolutionary anti-delinquency collar, don't cut out lurid newspaper articles about rampaging minors; get hard statistics from official sources, because they may tell a significantly different story.

Danger!

Consumer surveys - even if done professionally - should never be used as the sole basis of a decision to go ahead with a new product, because for reasons hinted at above they're no guide at all to people's actual buying behaviour. We'd go so far as to say that they're nearly always misleading, giving results that are often the exact opposite of the truth. Though they may yield useful general data about reaction to a product or problem, the opinion of experienced professionals who know what makes a product sell should always be given precedence. The only way to find out how potential consumers behave when faced with your product is to have the real thing there to sell - a strategy dealt with later - but even then you can be in trouble if you don't sell it in the right way, and especially if you ignore expert advice.

Don't be like the inventor of what we'll call a shopping accessory, who diligently questioned hundreds of shoppers about his product. The majority were so approving that he went ahead and manufactured some to sell at the price his survey indicated would be acceptable. He sold none; the exercise was a disaster. He was then introduced to a buyer for a major supermarket who offered to try the product out in a few branches as long as the price was cut to 99 pence. Her opinion was that it wouldn't sell for more. The inventor rejected the offer on the grounds that at 99 pence he couldn't make a profit out of the trial. But he wasn't going to make a loss either; he would just about break even. There was no risk if the product didn't take off, and if it did the huge orders that the supermarket would then place would drive down the unit cost of manufacture and he'd make a very healthy profit. For the sake of short-term greed he turned down a heaven-sent opportunity to test market his product for free in exactly the right environment. Some years on, the product still hasn't sold in any significant quantity.

On the positive side, this story also shows that a flop may be turned into a winner by changing a detail. That detail is most usually price, but it could equally be design, packaging, image, advertising, positioning or some more subtle factor. (A US company once launched a cake mix that only needed water adding. It bombed because housewives didn't like being left out of the action. The company removed the dried egg and relaunched it as a mix that just needed water *and an egg.* Result: vast sales.) Many seasoned entrepreneurs make fortunes by looking for failing products or businesses and turning them round, so if at first you don't succeed. . . look at your product again, or get someone else to look at it.

Market information sources

Market research is mainly data-gathering slog which then forms the basis of intelligent guesswork. A huge amount of market and company data is easily accessible and either free or cheap, so all you mostly need is time and patience.

Business information is increasingly available on the Internet, but an excellent resource is the library of any university which runs business and marketing courses, especially former polytechnics. They will have general guides and indexes to marketing data to orient you, and many industry-specific journals, directories, company reports, product statistics and market surveys. Better still, some libraries publish free subject guides to their reference material. It's a courtesy to introduce yourself to staff, especially if you need help to find your way around. If you're not a student you can usually use the facilities but may not be allowed to borrow. That shouldn't be a problem as long as you can take notes and use a photocopier where copyright law permits.

A university or college may also be able to provide market research assistance (as well as technical assistance - see Chapter 3). Many marketing courses require students to carry out 'real life' projects which amount to the equivalent of several weeks' work. It may be possible to turn part of your market research into such a project *if it meets teaching criteria.* There is usually a tutor in charge of project selection; ask library staff how to make contact.

If your proposal is accepted you'll have to spend time preparing a project brief and talking to the student. There is usually no fee, though you may have to pay some or all expenses. The advantages are the time you save and the free use of virtually professional expertise, especially useful for skilled primary research such as interviews and questionnaires. (Who knows, the student may see career potential in your idea and become a long-term ally!) The downside is that students differ in ability and projects tend to be confined to term time. Performance and outcomes can never be guaranteed, but most projects yield something of value.

Another avenue to explore is trade fairs and exhibitions in the UK and (if you can afford it) abroad. Most industries have their own events, which can be so important that companies gear sales campaigns and product launches to them, so find out dates and venues, acquire a ticket - usually free, but not readily available outside the industry - and be there. Ask discreet questions, make contacts, fill your plastic bag with brochures, look and learn. It can be a wonderful opportunity to poke at rival products and find out who does what.

If there is only one major annual event where buyers gather, that may effectively be your product launch deadline. Each one you miss is another year lost, so make it a key date in your development project scheduling.

To go on, or not to go on

Circumstances will dictate how much reaction to your idea you can safely get from manufacturers, stockists, buyers or end-users. Most will be unable or unwilling to comment without more detail than you dare disclose. Though access to the horse's mouth can be a big help - and essential if other research methods don't provide enough data - it is generally best to wait until you've got a prototype, a presentation 'act' and some legal protection sorted out. Your judgment on whether to go beyond this stage may therefore have to depend largely on gut feeling, so make sure your other research has been sufficiently thorough to give your gut plenty to digest.

Chapter 3
Proving your idea works

Prototypes, models, trial batches

If you're wondering when the real expense starts, it could be here. To stand any chance of persuading companies, financial backers or key buyers that your idea is technically sound and marketable, you must be able to prove that it works *and that you have done all you reasonably can to perfect it.* This is because companies much prefer ideas with as few unresolved problems as possible. You may see only a few loose ends that shouldn't take much tying; an experienced company or investor may instead see a knotty problem that might still be unravelled many costly man-hours later.

Many inventors don't appreciate the large difference between what it takes simply to *make* a product and what it takes to *manufacture* it efficiently and profitably in large numbers. Bridging that gap usually involves at least partial and often total redesign. The greater the redesign requirement, the higher will be the cost to the company and the less certain the outcome. This may cause companies and investors to turn you down *even if they like the product and think it will sell.* You therefore need to create something as close to a finished product as you can manage or afford.

You will also have to protect your idea, perhaps at some expense, as it takes physical shape and becomes known to others. See Chapter 6.

Assuming you've already tested your idea to your own

satisfaction using any cheap or scrap materials to hand (the first hovercraft was cobbled together using tin cans and a vacuum cleaner), here are your options:

❶ **Trial batches of product or near-product**

Best choice if it's feasible and you can afford it. You've got real product to show; with multiple samples to leave around you can speed up assessment; and you'll learn a lot about manufacturing costs, which can help enormously during presentations and negotiations. It will be essential for a product which companies need to damage or destroy during testing if they're to assess it fully. Unless you can make trial batches yourself, get some legal protection or approach designers and manufacturers only if they sign a confidentiality agreement. If cost is a problem, it may be worth exploring the possibilities of a joint development venture with a small local company - see Chapter 14.

Near-product is what you get when compromises are made to make the exercise affordable. For example: the tooling for an injection moulded plastic product normally costs many thousands of pounds, but it may be possible to commission a cheap makeshift mould that lasts long enough to produce a limited number of acceptable samples.

An impressive touch is professional point-of-sale packaging for your samples, but this is usually expensive and not strictly necessary.

❷ **Full-size prototype or scale working model**

Full size is best unless your product is so big that no one would reasonably expect you to lug it around. As far as you can, use materials, relative weights and proportions that would be used in manufacture. Cannibalize real products if they help make your prototype look good -

for example, for a power tool use the plastic casing of an existing tool. (Or use standard casings, readily available for many types of product.) If your product is huge but you still need a full-size prototype, a local factory might loan you fabrication space or do the job for you on reasonable terms. It's worth a try and could lead to a useful partnership.

❸ Rough working prototype plus non-working model

If money is tight or if the ideal materials or components are hard to obtain in small quantities, use any cheap materials for the prototype as long as the result adequately demonstrates the working principles of your idea, and present it alongside a model of what you think the product should look like. Use any cheap workable material - for example, painted wood for plastic. Beware the cost of professional model makers, as good ones aren't cheap and you could end up spending as much on a model as you might spend on a polished prototype. Try colleges or universities which run design technology courses; staff, students or technicians may be able to help at modest cost, especially if your project meets academic criteria.

❹ A short video

More a support prop than a substitute for any of the above, but useful if:

- Your product has a lengthy operating cycle.
- Demonstrating your product requires a site visit or a special environment.
- To demonstrate your product adequately you have to show people using it.
- Your prototype is temperamental.
- Your product needs to be seen by personnel not at the initial meeting.

- You need to record a special demonstration: for example, comparative trials of your prototype and competing products.

Don't bother with professionals unless you're staging a once-only event where without their expertise you risk making a pig's ear of it. Colleges running video production courses might offer student resources cheaply. Edit the video to no longer than three or four minutes (so it doesn't over-occupy a typical first meeting of 30-45 minutes), with or without a commentary. No jokes. No music. No special effects. No hamming. Just point the camera.

Although a video can be extremely useful, tapes can be easily copied and count as disclosure so (a) make sure your idea has some legal protection first and (b) don't include close-ups of the original or patentable elements of your idea.

❺ Other support materials

Consider any of the following if relevant; they can add persuasive force to presentations and demonstrations but are not a substitute for a product, prototype or model:

- **Product packaging**
  Effective but expensive to do well, and only worth considering if you've got a finished or near-finished product.

- **An artist's impression**
  Builders use them to sell developments that are still on the drawing board, so why shouldn't you? Ask an architect to recommend someone, as creating a detailed perspective sketch from technical drawings and/or photographs is a specialist skill.

- **A draft leaflet or brochure**
  This can illustrate how you envisage the product being marketed. It should strongly feature the benefits of the product and perhaps include instructions for use. It fulfills the dual purpose of impressing companies with your market-oriented thinking, and spelling out to them what your product does and why it's so good. Any computer with design or DTP software should produce something passable. For layout ideas, crib from existing (preferably non-related) product brochures.

Testing and assessment by companies

Before designing or making your prototype:

- **Find out how it's likely to be tested by companies**
  Most products have to be tested for robustness in normal use and abuse; for example, hand-held or small portable electronic equipment might reasonably have to withstand being dropped on the floor from desk height. It obviously helps if even a prototype can pass such tests. Products like anti-theft devices may have to be tested to destruction, in which case you need either a supply of samples or the test report of a reputable independent organisation such as a university. (Having both is even better.) Most universities will test commercial products at affordable rates, but you may have to hunt around to find a department with suitable test facilities.

  As a general rule don't rely on getting your prototype back in its original condition. Most companies are not wantonly cruel to prototypes but testing for durability and endurance can create natural wear and tear, so if you can only afford one prototype make sure you design in enough sturdiness to keep it soldiering on. Pray that you don't come up against a company like the building firm that tested the only sample of an inventor's scaffold clamp until it broke, then tossed the bits in the scrap bin and avoided telling him the truth for months. By then his patent application was about to lapse, but without a prototype he hadn't a hope of raising last minute interest from any other company.

- **Find out what statutory or industry standards your product might have to meet**
  Products increasingly have to meet recognized safety or performance standards before they can be sold or before people will buy them. Many standards are international, but some countries may demand additional or different standards. Competing products usually bear standards approval somewhere on the product or packaging, but do your own checks as not all the relevant standards may be included. The British Standards Institution, an industry body or a trading standards department may be able to advise you. Your prototype may have to demonstrate at least the potential to meet appropriate standards if it is to interest companies.

  If you intend to market your own product and it has to meet certain standards, the test fees of recognized certificating bodies will be a significant and often very large item in your costings. There may also be a lengthy wait before your product can be tested or before approval is granted.

Help with design or redesign

Design is the key to turning a rough functional prototype into a much slicker pre-production prototype, then a marketable product. You must think about design from the very start, as even an extremely well-built functional prototype may not impress companies if the underlying design is impractical or inappropriate. The true value of your invention may not be spotted if it's buried inside a poor design.

Good design determines *how well* a product works, and its importance to an invention can't be stressed too much. You may have invented a solution to a problem, but in doing so you will have created multiple problems of practical detail associated with turning an idea into a marketable product. Only someone with appropriate design skills can solve them.

If you don't have engineering or product design skills, or drawing skills to enable the invention to be properly understood by someone competent to make it, you may not be able to get even to functional prototype stage unaided. You have three options.

❶ If you can afford the substantial fees you can commission all the design you need from specialists - but agree in writing how large a share of the resulting intellectual property they're entitled to. This can come back to haunt you if not sorted out early.

❷ You may be able to bring a designer on board as a partner, for a share of the potential spoils rather than direct fees. But you must accept that if his or her work substantially improves your product, it may justify a large *and perhaps majority* share of your profits. You can easily end up in a crippling legal and financial dispute if you don't agree terms in advance and in writing. *It has to be said that inventors typically undervalue the input of designers. Many good inventions would be commercially worthless without a designer's contribution.*

❸ You may be able to get design assistance on budget terms by approaching the relevant technology department of a university (or a design counsellor at a Business Link: see Chapter 5). There are often DTI or

EU-subsidised schemes which make the design expertise of academic staff available at low cost to small businesses and occasionally individuals; or it may be possible, as with market research, to turn your design requirement into a student project at even lower cost but with a less certain outcome. Universities these days can be extremely helpful to small businesses, so don't be afraid to approach them; but be open and co-operative, try to be specific about what you want, and accept the restraints of academic timetables.

An experienced designer can be invaluable in dealings with manufacturers, either at prototype or full production stage. Manufacturers need detailed and precise specifications before they can make anything, and if queries or problems arise they need access to someone who talks their language. If you're not up to those demands, you must use a designer.

Getting quotations from manufacturers

Shop around, as manufacturing costs can vary widely. Small firms may be better for prototypes and trial batches, as large companies with advanced equipment may be cheaper only at very high volume (but for that reason get quotes from them too). Ask for quotes based on the detailed drawings you or your designer have produced *and make sure they represent exactly what you want. A late request for what seems like a minor modification can add enormously to the final bill.*

It doesn't harm to talk generally to manufacturers about production costs and how to reduce them. If they're interested in what you're doing, you can learn a lot from them. Get quotes for larger quantities in steps - for example 1000-off, 5000-off, 10,000-off - and run-on costs per thousand thereafter. This gives you an idea of what sort of quantities you need to be selling to get costs down and profits up.

Chapter 4
Taking stock

The story so far:

- Your idea seems to be original.
- It works, and you can prove it.
- There is a specific market to aim it at.
- To be competitive it must be priced at around £*x*.
- To make a decent profit you or a licensee must sell around *y* units a year.

It's now time to do some hard thinking. We've put this chapter here because it has to go somewhere, but you may need its guidance before reaching prototype stage if that's likely to be expensive, especially if it includes redesign or patent costs.

Before making any move that involves serious money or risk, consider another golden rule: *the potential reward from your idea must be much greater than the cost and risk involved in getting it on to the market.* It's fundamental common sense, but common sense is often an early casualty when inventors glimpse a fortune on the horizon. Chapter 12 deals with methods of calculating how much you might expect to get from your idea.

You need to see yourself making a good living for several years before taking a large gamble such as sinking all your savings into your idea. It may be worth going out on a limb for an idea aimed at, say, the automotive market if there's a prospect of huge worldwide sales. But a less profitable, low-volume market may not be worth any risk, no matter how good or virtuous the idea. If royalties are likely to be only a couple of hundred pounds a year, they may not even cover your annual patent renewal fees let alone the original costs.

(Regrettably, many aids for the disabled fall into this category, but if profit isn't your main concern try contacting organizations such as REHAB, an excellent voluntary body which helps bring aids for the disabled to fruition.)

Making a business of your invention

You're more likely to succeed if other people - primarily companies, potential investors and business support agencies - see you making a significant personal commitment to your idea. Without it you're unlikely to get any matching commitment from them. An inventor we know asked an enterprise body to help him set up a business. They spent weeks drawing up a business plan, locating premises and pulling in funding. But when the backers insisted that he devote himself full time to the business, it emerged that he was on sabbatical leave from a job he didn't want to quit. His commitment to his idea was zero and the project collapsed immediately.

Such cases are not rare, and they make advisers and backers justifiably wary of anyone who shows signs of wanting to be lifted and carried every inch of the way.

The lesson is that there is a large nettle you may have to grasp: *the best way to convince the world of your commitment may be to run the development of your idea as a business.* That needn't mean giving up your day job and hocking your house, unless you actually want a lifestyle with a radically different set of highs and lows. It's relatively easy to run a small business as a sideline (both authors of this book have done it), and even if you much prefer to license your idea to a company it can be a good idea to set up a temporary business with the limited aim of achieving and administering a licensing agreement.

The key advantages of operating as a business are:

- Many of your expenses become tax deductible.
- It puts your activities on a professional footing, which should make companies and professionals take you more seriously.
- It enables you to shed the deadly 'inventor' label.
- It gives you access to forms of help not normally available to individuals: grants, subsidies, technology support schemes, advice, training etc.
- It's the most convincing form of market research; if you succeed in making sales, you can show companies solid evidence of the value of your idea.
- It's easier to raise development funding as a business with some track record than as an individual with only optimism to offer.

For more detail, see Chapters 13 onwards. From here until Chapter 13 we focus on how to reach a licensing agreement with a company as that's the best option for most inventors and most inventions. **But our guidance reflects our belief that your chances of achieving a deal with a company may be significantly improved if you're prepared to assume some kind of entrepreneurial role, even if that falls short of starting a business. The record shows that most successsful inventors go out and open their own doors rather than wait passively for a company to let them in.**

Chapter 5
Getting help

Finding the right kind of help. . .

Developing a product demands a spread of skills that few individuals possess, so as the element of risk increases it's important not to attempt everything on your own. Stick to what you know or do well and use professionals for the rest.

But how much practical help is there specifically for inventors? Apart from patent agents, very little. Public sector innovation centres have done sterling work over the years, but the handful that survive usually lack the funds to bring more than a few inventions to fruition.

There is however plenty of help targeted at innovative small businesses, which you can utilize by becoming one. Schemes come and go, so it's futile to attempt to list them here. The best way to find out about them is to contact one of the Government-supported 'one-stop shops' set up to signpost all forms of subsidised or low-cost help. In England they're **Business Links**; find one locally by ringing (0345) 56776. In Scotland they're **Business Shops**; to find one, ring 0800 787878. In Wales the service is called **Business Connect** (why all these different names?!) and the number is (0345) 969798.

Additionally, contact the business development departments of councils in your area. Shop around; there may be an advantage in locating your business some distance from home, as the amount of enterprise funding available can differ widely from district to district. (Struggling areas tend to have more.) The key criterion is usually the local employment potential of your business, even if this amounts initially to only one or two jobs.

. . . and avoiding the wrong kind

Help you can do without includes commercial invention agencies which offer to place your invention for a hefty fee. They advertise widely - often calling themselves 'product developers' - but may contact you directly via the address on your patent application. All make large claims about what they can do, but if they do anything at all it may be no more than send brief details of your invention indiscriminately to companies, most of whom will treat it as junk mail. Some offer a genuine service but it still might not amount to anything you couldn't do yourself at far less cost.

Those based overseas, particularly in the USA, seem to be the worst. Tactics include flattering you into an 'urgent' meeting, usually at a hotel or some other temporary address where you're pressured into signing an agreement and parting with cash, typically thousands of pounds. The best advice is not to deal with any of them. Second-best advice is:

❶ Before any meeting:
- Check that their address exists and is permanent.
- Make them disclose *in writing* their fees and what you get for your money.
- Ask for documented proof of their success.
- Run a business credit check on them.

❷ During a meeting:
- Be prepared for a great deal of 'friendly' pressure.
- Never hand over money, even a deposit.
- If handed an agreement to sign on the spot, refuse. Insist on time to think and take it to a patent agent or solicitor for an opinion.

Watch out too for self-styled business or marketing consultants who offer help for fees typically in the £200-500 per day bracket. Many small businesses have been ruined by them. 'Consultant' has been cynically defined as someone who borrows your watch to tell you the time, but a bad one will tell you the wrong time and then keep your watch. Consultancy can be a last resort of redundant managers; when established companies won't touch them with a barge pole they may end up 'advising' start-up businesses in environments where by rights you ought to be safe.

Three examples - there are many more - illustrate how much of a menace they can be. One innovator was persuaded by a consultant to remortgage her house to buy expensive and unusable plastic injection moulding equipment when there were plenty of local plastic injection manufacturers perfectly capable of the work. Another let two consultants manage his start-up company. They milked off all the investment funding as 'expenses' and for months refused to let him see his own books. Then there was the consultant employed to run a local authority enterprise scheme who raised substantial grant funding for sixteen start-up businesses. Fine; except that he spent most of it on 'feasibility studies' carried out by a string of marketing companies that all turned out to be him. None of the start-ups survived.

Until you know your way around it can be difficult to tell good, bad and indifferent consultants apart, though the good ones will usually be too busy with larger clients to approach you. They'll all say you've got what they can cure: an IT specialist will prescribe an expensive computer system, a marketing specialist an expensive ad campaign, and so on. Those who offer to get grants for you are not miracle workers; they go through channels open to anyone, but a risk is that they may spice up the application with false information that could severely compromise you later.

Your best strategy is not to get into a position where you need someone whose contribution you can't assess or control. Take small steps you understand rather than big ones you don't; progress might be slower but it'll be a lot safer.

As a general rule: if anyone with what seems like the right stuff wants to pal up with you as associate, consultant or whatever:

- Ask yourself why; what can possibly be in it for him?
- Ask yourself what you stand to lose.
- Contact the business and social names he drops. Do they know him? Do they recommend him?
- Look for signs of a serious need for money - debt, divorce, drink etc.
- Test him. Ask him to do something small but useful. Does it happen?

If this all sounds a mite paranoid, remember that a business venture fronted by a raw beginner, and perhaps with a decent pot of start-up funding in the bank, is precisely the easy target some opportunists look for and all too often find.

Chapter 6
Intellectual property

Defining and protecting your idea

It now becomes important for you to:

- Define your intellectual property - the aspects of your idea that are novel and should belong to you.
- Establish an 'official' date of origin for your idea.
- Obtain the most appropriate form or forms of legal protection for it.

This is so that you have:

- Freedom to disclose the detail of your idea in relative safety.
- Something that you can sell and that others can buy or license from you.
- Possible (though not guaranteed) priority over other people with similar ideas.

It's also important to understand that your goal is to get your product successfully to market and that protecting your intellectual property is only one aspect of this.

This 'health warning' is needed because many inventors spend too much time and money on patenting and neglect aspects that are at least equally important, such as market research and technical development. They're so hooked on protecting *the idea* that *the product* and *the business opportunity* don't get a look-in. They convince themselves that once they've got a patent, all doors will fling themselves open. Nothing - or not much - is further from the truth. Inventors who embrace the patent system as though they're responding to a mating call are courting danger. We could cite plenty of inventors who willingly - even eagerly - drove themselves into inextricable debt in pursuit of patents that never earned them a penny. Getting a new product to market involves a concerted campaign on several fronts. Focus all your resources on one and you risk winning a battle only to lose the war. Although protecting your idea is a necessary step and may even be the key to your fortune, *it is not an end in itself.* You should have a clear view of where you are now and where you're heading before committing time and money to legal protection.

Meaning and importance of intellectual property

What are you actually trying to sell when you show your idea to companies? Certainly nothing physical. Your prototype is only a device to help people understand your idea, and in itself has no commercial value. What is of value is *the right to stop unauthorized people from using for gain the specific knowledge - the inventive step - that makes your idea in some way unique.*

That specific knowledge is your intellectual property. It has to be expressed in some suitable form so that the rights in it can be bought, sold, hired or exchanged in the same way as a physical commodity. It must also determine the precise limits of what you own, so that if you yourself can't commercially exploit your intellectual property it may be possible to reach a deal with someone who can.

Your intellectual property should consist of a written technical description accompanied by visual representations: technical drawings, sketches, photographs, computer simulations or all of these. (A prototype doesn't strictly count: it's simply an object made by using your intellectual property. But showing it may count as disclosure, so keep it under wraps until you have adequate protection.)

Your intellectual property should include an explanation of exactly what your invention does and how it works. In theory it should enable someone familiar with the appropriate technology - in legal terminology, someone 'skilled in the art' - to understand your invention well enough to physically make it. In practice you're describing your idea in outline only, so your drawings needn't be so technically detailed that a product can be made directly from them.

None the less, your overall description needs to be as clear and complete as you can make it. Any vagueness or ambiguity will make its commercial assessment more difficult, and may form a dangerous loophole in your legal protection. The more precisely you describe and define your intellectual property - and the best person to do this is your patent agent - the more easily can commercial or legal decisions be reached about it.

In most countries, including the UK, intellectual property ownership is recognized in law. *But that doesn't guarantee anything at all,* as you'll find as you read on.

Why do you need legal protection?

You need some form of legal protection so you can discuss your idea with other people. Disclosure is never wholly without risk even if your idea is legally protected, but a freer exchange of information means you'll probably make better progress on every front. Your idea will almost certainly need developing before it's saleable, and you'll only find out what needs to be done if you can talk openly to a range of people whose opinions matter or whose skill and experience can help you - manufacturers, potential buyers, marketing, technical and financial advisers etc.

If you disclose your idea before obtaining protection - through any act from an unguarded private conversation or letter to a very public press article or exhibition - it may be impossible to get adequate protection later. It will also range from hard to impossible to sell your idea, as the value of your intellectual property will be reduced if not wiped out. You will have put your inventive step partly or wholly in the public domain, free for anyone to use without paying you anything. (If all is not lost you may still be able to make and market your product at your own risk, but it won't be an auspicious start.)

Until you've taken steps to protect your idea, discuss it only in strict confidence and only with people who need to know. You needn't worry about patent agents, solicitors, Government officials, patent librarians and Patent Office staff, who are automatically bound to confidence by their professional codes. To deal with others not so bound, you need at least a confidentiality agreement: but getting companies in particular to sign them isn't easy (see **Confidentiality agreements** below).

Legal disputes

You also need competent and legally recognized protection so that if there is ever a dispute about your idea, answers can be found to these basic legal questions:

- **Who owns the idea?**
  You, presumably - but perhaps not if it's directly related to your employment. If you're in a job where you might contractually or reasonably be expected to contribute new ideas, the intellectual property may belong rightfully to your employer. If there's any doubt you must discuss it with them - but first take the precaution of protecting the idea in your own name, and take independent legal advice.

- **What is the date of origin of the idea?**
  Dates of origin can be crucial. If two people come up with very similar ideas, priority is given to the one who can prove he had his idea first - or who filed first in the case of an idea protected by patent. (Except in the USA, where it's who invented first, not who filed first. See **Patenting in the USA** later in this chapter.)

- **Is the idea really original?**
  People who copy your product will say in their defence that the idea isn't original even though it may have been granted a patent. If that is accepted, your patent will be either void or all but useless. To have a defence you need to ensure that the original features of your idea are clearly and adequately described in your intellectual property.

- **How does the idea work?**
  An idea is hard to protect, and later to defend, if it isn't clear how it works - a particular danger if you file your own patent application. A comprehensive technical description of your invention, written (ideally by a patent agent) in appropriate language and with specific reference to clear technical drawings, is essential if your intellectual property is to be worth anything.

Know-how

It's worth saying a few words here about know-how, a term more or less synonymous with 'tricks of the trade' or 'trade secrets' In your case it means unique knowledge you have acquired through experience but which you don't need to disclose in a patent. It can be incalculably valuable. Take Coca-Cola™ for example. Its principal ingredients are fairly well known; what is secret is the exact formula: how much of what gives you a drink identical to Coca-Cola.™ That is the

Coke know-how, and its commercial value can only be guessed at. At a more lowly level, you may have saleable know-how if over time you have learned, for example, that you get better results if you use raw material from a particular source, or you can cheapen a process if you use equipment in an unconventional way.

If you have any, know-how can constitute an important part of your intellectual property and can be sold or licensed even if you don't have a patent. It can also be a powerful bargaining counter. See later chapters on licensing and negotiation for more detail.

The problem with know-how is that although your ownership of it can be recognised in law, there is no way of registering it and its theft - usually by employees or associates - can be hard to establish. It's therefore up to you to ensure that your commercial secrets are both secure and documented in such a way that you are clearly identified as their owner.

Forms of legal protection

The law provides several distinct forms of protection for intellectual property, dealt with separately below. From the cost-conscious inventor's point of view they divide into those which are free (confidentiality, copyright and design right) and those which involve official fees and for which you generally also need the services of a patent agent (design registration, trade mark and patent).

It's vital to understand that YOU are responsible for enforcing any form of protection. (Governments worldwide are making strenuous efforts to stamp out counterfeiting, but until your product is a major brand name this may not be much comfort.) However, most companies do respect intellectual property rights, so an exchange of correspondence between patent agents may be all that is necessary to settle a dispute.

Legal costs insurance can be bought (see later) but it covers you only if an assessor estimates your prospects of winning at better than even. In addition, a Patents County Court now exists which provides a much cheaper forum for settling patent and design disputes. Even so, a patent infringement dispute going to trial is still expected to cost each party several thousand pounds. This ought to make you pause for very deep thought about just how different your idea is from other ideas, and how much that difference is really worth.

We can only treat the different forms of protection briefly. In the case of patents this isn't just necessary, it's deliberate; the subject is so vast that if you want to satisfy your interest you really must read more specialized literature. Rest assured, there's plenty of it.

Here then are the different forms of protection available:

• CONFIDENTIALITY AGREEMENTS

Confidentiality agreements have two uses. One is as sole protection for an idea that isn't much more than a thought - for example, a new way to market an existing product. If you want to sell such an idea to someone capable of exploiting it, *get a confidentiality agreement signed before disclosing anything.* This is because an idea that can't be given any kind of uniquely identifiable two- or three-dimensional form is one of the hardest things to protect. Even if you write it down, copyright (see below) may not be much use as it only protects the words you write from being copied and doesn't protect the thinking that lies behind them. But if someone signs your confidentiality agreement and then uses your idea without permission or payment, you may be able to sue for breach of confidence. This was done successfully some years ago by the originators of an idea which became a popular TV series.

The other use is much wider; a confidentiality agreement can be used to protect any idea *in conjunction with or as a precursor to other forms of protection.* In theory you can draft your own confidentiality agreement for nothing, then discuss your idea in relative safety with anyone willing to sign it. It's a good way to make progress with your idea in the early stages, when you're still researching its potential and don't yet know if more expensive protection is justified.

In practice there is a problem. It isn't so much that people will break confidence, but that many companies, especially large ones, won't sign confidentiality agreements. Their motive is self-protection; it may be difficult to discuss your idea without disclosing sensitive information of their own. Their fears are reasonable: if it was that easy to get them to open up, they'd be overrun by industrial spies touting bogus inventions.

Some companies may compromise by demanding an exchange

of confidentiality agreements. This is perfectly reasonable, but check their agreement carefully before signing to make sure it doesn't unreasonably restrict your own future activities.

The best way to persuade companies and individuals to sign your confidentiality agreement is to draft one that doesn't scare them off. There's no set formula, so it's quite acceptable to write your own. *Whatever you include in it, remember that your main objective is to get people to sign it.* A short, simple document may be full of danger for both parties if too much is left unspecified, while a long one bristling with restrictive clauses and legal jargon is unlikely to attract many signatures. This model - included for guidance only - is, in our view, pitched at about the right level:

NON-DISCLOSURE AGREEMENT

Parties to the Agreement:

[Company name and address]
[Your name and address]

Basis of the Agreement:

1 On the understanding that both parties are interested in meeting to consider possible collaboration in developments arising from [your name]'s intellectual property it is agreed that the information, documents and material supplied in the course and as a result of so meeting shall be treated as confidential.

2 This confidentiality applies to both technical and commercial information which either party may communicate to the other.

3 Excepted from this undertaking of confidentiality is any information in the public domain or which the receiving

party can show was already in his possession prior to its disclosure.

4 Either party to this Agreement shall on request from the other return any documents or items connected with the disclosure and shall not retain any unauthorized copies or likenesses.

5 After five years from the date hereof each party shall be relieved of all obligations under this Agreement.

Signed [Your signature]
For [Your business/trading name if relevant]
Date
Signed [Company representative's signature]
For [Company name]
Date

You can soften your approach by including something like this in your covering letter:

> As you will appreciate, it is important that all exchanges of information should at this stage be in confidence. I therefore enclose a copy of a Non-disclosure Agreement which I have drafted and hope you will find acceptable.
>
> For my own part, I shall be happy to sign your own confidentiality agreement assuming its conditions are broadly similar to mine.

Even then you may not be out of the woods. The fear among big firms especially is that they could already be working on a similar idea, so they may want evidence of a patent or patent application to avoid any argument about dates and content. *They may refuse to discuss in confidence anything but a patent,* and could even insist on your signing a document stating that they *won't* be held to confidentiality - though in practice they may well respect it. It's up to you to decide whether to accept the risk.

• COPYRIGHT

Copyright gives limited but worthwhile protection against the unauthorized copying or adapting of drawn, written or photographic descriptions of your invention.

As long as all the work is clearly your own and not copied from someone else, copyright arises automatically, so in theory you needn't do anything special to get it. But it's usually associated with published works such as novels, plays and music, and in your case you're still a long way from public disclosure. You therefore need to carry out the simple procedure described below to back up any claim of originality you may need to make.

Even if you plan to patent your invention, carry out this procedure as soon as possible - and as often as necessary as you develop and significantly improve your idea. There is no risk, and it establishes an earlier date of origin than a patent application would give you. Should there ever be a dispute about origin, this date could be invaluable.

What you need to do:

❶ Make sketches or drawings of your product or invention. If you have a model or prototype, photograph it or even video it. Write down any text which someone else would need to copy to make use of your idea - for example a computer program or rules of a game. Then write your name on each document, including any later modifications to drawings or text.

❷ Place all documents (*originals only* - photocopies or carbons won't do, so take all the copies you need for your own continued use) in an envelope sealed in a tamper-proof way. For example, cover the glued flaps at *both* ends of the envelope with strong parcel tape.

❸ Then get someone whose word is likely to carry weight in court to certify on the envelope that it was sealed on the stated date when he or she examined it; or mail the envelope to yourself by registered post, and keep the dated Post Office receipt. Keep both in a safe place *and don't ever open the envelope.* A traditional option is to lodge the envelope with a bank or solicitor and get a dated receipt, but experience suggests that most banks and many solicitors aren't keen to offer this service.

The point of doing all this is to *establish a date at which the copyright material was known to exist.* Though dates aren't as crucial as they are if you're applying for a patent or registered design, a clearly recorded date will help a court to reach a decision if you ever need to defend your copyright.

(We're assuming that your copyright material isn't being made available to the public. If it is, it helps - though it's not strictly necessary - to declare your copyright on all published material relating to your idea. Simply print your name, followed by the familiar © symbol and the year of publication.)

Advantages and disadvantages

Copyright is recognized internationally, doesn't need renewing and lasts until 70 years after your death. There are no official fees or application formalities. Any drawing or sketch you make and any text you write (including computer programs) is automatically covered. Anyone who without your permission copies or adapts your drawings or text, or handles such copies, infringes your copyright and can be taken to court.

However, copyright doesn't protect your idea; it only protects the particular form in which you express it. Nor does it protect your product, but only the drawing or other illustration on which it is based. It also only protects against deliberate copying, and won't necessarily protect you if another person innocently comes up with a very similar idea. This may quite easily happen, as there is no official copyright register and thus no possibility of carrying out a search as you can with patents.

Copyright on its own gives you no protection if someone can use your idea without having to copy it. None the less, it may be sufficient protection if the income from your invention is likely to be small. If your idea isn't worth patenting it probably isn't worth stealing. It may be better to try to negotiate an amicable profit-sharing deal with a copyright infringer than take him to court and risk bankrupting both of you.

• DESIGN RIGHT

Design right protects the design of three-dimensional articles. It applies to the original and non-commonplace design of any aspect of the shape or configuration of an article - internal or external, in whole or in part.

It doesn't cover surface decorations or two-dimensional designs, which are better protected by copyright and/or design registration. It won't give you a monopoly right, but does give you a right to prevent copying. It lasts for 10 years after articles made to the design are first marketed, subject to a maximum of 15 years' protection from the date you created the design. But during the last five years, anyone will be entitled to a licence from you, with *or without* your co-operation, to make and sell articles copying the design.

Design right excludes so-called 'must fit' and 'must match' features, where parts of one article are determined by the design of another. This mainly affects the design of spare parts, for example car engine gaskets ('must fit') and car body panels ('must match').

It operates in many ways like copyright. You don't apply - it arises automatically when the design is created, but you should follow the copyright self-registration procedure to provide yourself with evidence of a priority date. (In terms of the action you need to take, copyright and design right are identical, so you needn't do everything twice.)

Advantages and disadvantages

Like copyright, design right is free. But its protection doesn't last as long and covers you in fewer countries - small help if your product has a world market. Another drawback, as with copyright, is that there is no official register in which your design can appear. It's therefore inadvisable to rely on design right alone to protect a product with substantial potential.

• DESIGN REGISTRATION

Design registration protects only the visual appearance (or 'eye appeal' in the wording of the Designs Act) of an object. It's administered by the Designs Registry at the Patent Office, to whom you can write for an application form. There are parallels with patent procedure, but the process is quicker (4-6 months), less complex and cheaper. Protection is for a maximum of 25 years and the initial fee covers the first five.

In law, design has four features: *shape* and *configuration* (three-dimensional), *pattern* and *ornament* (two-dimensional). As with patents the main official test is for novelty. Drawings, known as representations, are central to the application. Adequate protection depends on giving your design the broadest possible definition, and on submitting separate applications for its different elements. An application for an important feature, such as the distinctive shape of a bottle, is then less likely to be jeopardized by the non-originality of a less important feature such as a decoration on the bottle. A patent agent is qualified to advise you on this.

Advantages and disadvantages

Action can be taken against anyone who makes, sells, uses or imports articles which closely resemble the article registered. As usual, you must decide whether you can afford court action. Design registration is relatively cheap and straightforward, but getting a really useful registration takes skill, so consider using a patent agent. Also, if you're in an industry where illicit copying thrives globally, infringement may be hard to detect and even harder to prosecute.

Design registration is not a cheap substitute for a patent. Consider it only if the outward appearance of your invention is going to be its main selling feature. Even so, it may be little help if you're not in a position to fight experienced commercial pirates.

- TRADE MARK

If you intend to market your own product you'll need a trade mark: in the words of the Trade Marks Act 1994, 'any sign which is capable of distinguishing [the] goods and services of a trader and can be represented graphically'. That can cover words, images, three-dimensional shapes, slogans, even colours. Because a trade mark can be valid indefinitely (subject to renewal every ten years) if correctly used and maintained, and can outlive patent, design or copyright protection, it might end up as your most valuable asset. *It won't however protect the product as such, so you also need some other protection.*

Trade marks can be registered at the Trade Mark Registry (part of the Patent Office) provided they comply with certain statutory requirements. However, the mere fact that your proposed trade mark is registrable doesn't necessarily mean it will appeal to potential customers, so put plenty of thought and research effort into developing a trade mark appropriate to the product and its market. Names are particularly important but coining one that is apt, distinctive and original isn't easy. It may be worth paying a marketing design company to develop a registrable identity for your product.

You can apply for registration yourself, but may be better advised to use a patent or a registered trade mark agent (most patent agents are both).

And before you commit yourself, the Patent Office's Search and Advisory Service may be able to save you money and problems: it can advise you on the registrability of your proposed trade mark, and for a fee can carry out an infringement clearance search to check that your proposed trade mark is not an inadvertent steal of someone else's.

Advantages and disadvantages

A trade mark is probably not an issue if you intend to license your idea to a company, but if you want to market your own product or service could you afford *not* to have one? Brands which become household names can be worth more than the company that makes the product, so registering a trade mark could be the shrewdest move you ever make. Its efficacy and value depend however on *how well it sells the product*, which registration cannot influence. Nor does a trade mark protect the product or service itself. If you have to fund a patent or registered design as well, a trade mark is an added expense at a time when you least need it.

• PATENT

If your idea is a true invention, consisting wholly or partly of something new and previously unthought of, and - far more important - has demonstrably good commercial prospects, then you should consider applying for a patent *when the time is right.*

A patent is a form of legal monopoly granted by the Crown, or its equivalent in other countries, in return for public disclosure of your invention. A UK patent lasts for 20 years, but only if annual renewal fees are paid. Patent systems exist in most countries, and their intention is always the same: to encourage the disclosure and commercial use of new ideas.

If you want chapter and verse on the technicalities of patenting - which is essentially a huge field of international law that gets heavier and muddier the deeper you dig into it - this isn't the book for you. We'll restrict ourselves to this: at the heart of the patent system is the concept of *claims.* In theory the inventor says 'I claim that my idea is original and belongs to me, and I'd like the world to recognize both those facts'. The world - represented by the patent system - then either agrees or disagrees. In practice it ain't so easy. Though you may appear to get a patent for the whole of your idea, you more accurately get a patent for only *the parts* of your idea that patent examiners accept may be original.

It makes sense, as most inventions borrow from existing technologies, the rights to which - if there are any - belong to someone else. If, for example, you invent a device powered by standard batteries, you can't claim the batteries or battery connections as part of your intellectual property; but if the batteries are housed in a novel way that is unique to your idea, you *might* be able to claim for the housing.

You or your patent agent must therefore break your idea down into as many separate elements of originality as possible, and make a separate claim for each. Your application is thus, in effect, a list of claims supported by a technical description. The official examiner then looks at each claim separately and either allows it or disallows it.

Few applicants have all their claims accepted, so one of the skills in drafting a patent application is to identify the maximum number of worthwhile claims that can be 'mined' from one idea. It's rather like tadpoles and frogs: you need an awful lot of tadpoles to get an adequate number of frogs.

You can study the claims process by looking back at a few published applications and comparing the claims made in them with the claims that survive in the actual patent. Even then, the claims left may be so weak that the patent has little or no commercial value.

Are all inventions patentable? No. An idea is patentable only if it is *all* of these:

- New and previously undisclosed.
- Distinguished by an inventive step not obvious to one skilled in the art - that is, someone with skill or experience in the relevant technology or industry.
- Capable of industrial application - that is, it could actually be made or used and isn't just a flight of fancy or a physical impossibility.

Things that can't be patented include scientific theories, literary works, music, offensive or anti-social devices and anti-gravity or perpetual motion machines. Computer programs *as such* can't be patented, but it's perfectly possible to get a patent for a technical process or system that is implemented by your software. This is however one of those areas of swirling grey where expert legal advice is vital.

Advantages and disadvantages

The main advantages of a patent are:

- It's usually essential for an idea likely to be worth a lot of money (assuming, of course, that it's patentable in the first place).
- From first application, your idea can be disclosed to other people, enabling faster development.

However, the disadvantages are daunting. The full application process can take years, yet still come to nothing. It is too complex for most individuals to tackle unaided, and so can be expensive in patent agents' fees. Patent renewal fees, which you have to pay every year for up to 20 years, begin at about £100 and increase with successive years. Patent cover in other countries can multiply your costs many times over. You have to police your own patent and tackle infringers at your own expense. And your patent can be challenged by anyone at any time and will, if the challenge is successful, be at worst declared void and at best reduced in value.

Also, in any field a competitor may possess what is termed a 'dominating patent' occupying the general area in which your patent is based. It's often used as a deliberate blocking tactic to stop others working their inventions. This is a case where it's virtually essential to have your own patent to act as a bargaining counter.

Look into the workings of the patent system thoroughly before making any moves, and take professional advice about your chances of obtaining a worthwhile patent. Find out how much you'll have to spend getting and renewing a patent, and set that against an objective estimate of the commercial value of your product over the same period.

If your product isn't likely to repay its patenting costs many times over, it's unlikely to be of much interest to a company. It's thus unlikely to be worth more than perhaps an application and refiling in order to buy some extra time (see stage ❹ in **How to apply for a UK patent** later) while you try to market the product yourself. If you have money to spare, it may be worth gambling the cost of a full UK patent, but not the far greater cost of multiple foreign patent applications.

Putting patents into perspective

Although a patent is the widest and for many ideas the only effective form of protection available, it doesn't always live up to its inflated reputation in the public imagination. The following list isn't intended to put you off patents entirely, but so many misconceptions surround them that if you do decide to apply for one, you need to be absolutely sure you're doing it for the right reasons:

- Full application is an unavoidably long, complex and expensive process. If it costs more than any potential royalty income or trading profit, or diverts you from selling or developing your idea, it will harm rather than help your prospects.

- A patent will not on its own get your idea to market. *Most patented inventions never become products, because no one wants them.* That's why market research is vital.

- A patent is supposed to protect your idea, but it can have the opposite effect. In the UK, patent applications are automatically published after 18 months; a form of disclosure that you can't duck unless you withdraw your application or go to the trouble of filing exclusively in the USA (see **Patenting in the USA** later) where applications are not published. Many companies - particularly in south-east Asia - search the patent system routinely to alert them to promising developments. It may be easy for someone to re-work the inventive step in your published application in a way that won't infringe your patent.

- The granting of a patent doesn't mean the Patent Office approves of your idea. All it signifies is that your idea seems for the time being to be original and contains an inventive step. The main purpose of patents isn't to make patentees rich, but to encourage investment in new technologies.
- A patent isn't necessarily yours for keeps; anyone can challenge it at any time and you may have to defend it at your own cost. If the challenge succeeds, you lose all or some (usually the best bits) of your patent.
- *There is no such thing as a world patent.* A UK patent only protects you in the UK. Filing foreign patents is extremely expensive and complex, although doing it via the Patent Co-operation Treaty (see **Foreign patents** later) can defer some of the heavier costs by 18 months. In general, multiple foreign patenting should only be considered if there is proven commercial justification. Professional advice is essential when making the decision.
- A patent ultimately offers little protection if you can't afford to enforce it. No official body will fight or finance your legal battles, or even check whether anyone is infringing your patent.

If tempted, as so many inventors are, to rush out before dawn's early light and get yourself a patent, think long and hard around these two key points:

❶ Your idea needs the best *appropriate* protection. Don't dismiss other options as necessarily inferior. For many ideas a patent is the least appropriate (though certainly the most expensive) form of protection.

❷ The later you can file, the easier you sleep at nights. From the moment you file an application a clock starts ticking remorselessly (see points ❷ and ❸ in **How to apply for a UK patent** later). File too early and you could all too soon be running a frantic and doomed race to licence your idea to a company before you become liable for very heavy patenting costs.

Patent agents

A patent is both a technical and a legal document and the patent system is highly complex. Though there is a limited but useful amount you can do for yourself, there quickly comes a point where it is false economy not to engage a patent agent to act for you. He or she can improve your chances of obtaining a worthwhile patent and can help you avoid many pitfalls. On the other hand, no patent agent can guarantee that your patent will provide you with licensable intellectual property or result in a commercially successful product. That depends entirely on the merits of your idea and on your own efforts to exploit it. If neither is enough, your agent's fees will simply make your loss heavier.

At a pinch you can draft your own application, but you may run a serious risk of leaving loopholes for others to wriggle through. Also, a 'home-made' specification may have reduced impact when you're trying to market your idea: another factor that can make a professionally drafted application a good investment. You can to some extent have your cake and eat it; many patent agents are well aware of the financial problems inventors face, and can often improve a self-drafted application before the end of the first 12 months, *but only if it has (a) a complete and detailed description of the invention and (b) good drawings.*

Patent agents observe confidentiality at all times; like solicitors, they risk claims against them if they're negligent in any way. If they think you're following the wrong course of action they'll tell you, but ultimately they follow your instructions. It may be wise to start by asking your agent to give you a brief professional opinion of whether your invention will be patentable, based on your own patent search findings. You'll have to pay for this, but it will be money well spent. Bear in mind though that *it won't and can't include any indication of commercial potential.*

Patent agents don't of course just draft applications. They're qualified to advise on all intellectual property matters, and on the forms of protection available in the UK or abroad for any idea or innovation. Many are also experienced in commercial aspects such as technology transfer and negotiating and drafting licensing agreements. They can also act when disputes arise, for example over alleged infringements.

Look in Yellow Pages® for local patent agents or write to the Chartered Institute of Patent Agents (CIPA: see **Useful addresses**) for a full list. At your first meeting discuss how much you may have to pay and what you get for it. CIPA operates a scheme under which its members will give 45 minutes' advice and guidance free of charge. If you prepare your questions you can cover a lot of ground in that time, so it's an offer you should certainly take advantage of!

How to apply for a UK patent

First and most important, *resist the temptation to apply for a patent as soon as you've had your idea.* Use copyright and/or design right and confidentiality agreements to acquire some useful free protection and proof of origin, and wait until your research into your idea's originality and commercial potential is complete. You will then be in a much better position to judge whether a patent application is justified.

Biding your time increases the risk that someone else will beat you to it, but patenting is as much a game of tactics as a legal process and delayed filing has plenty of precedent as a smart move. Some companies will spend years developing a product, yet not file an application almost until the eve of launch. They weigh the risk of losing priority against the risk that publication of their application will forewarn competitors and enable them to rush out their own new or improved products. In your case you have to weigh the risk of losing priority against that of losing all your money in patent costs before you can get it back again in royalties or trading profits.

Unless you're prepared to adopt the risky strategy of refiling your application, you have one year *before incurring substantial patent costs (see application stages ❷ - ❹ below). Few products can be developed to licensing or launch stage in that time.* **No matter how good your idea is, protecting your personal finances must be your absolute priority.** *It may therefore be in your best interests to delay filing for as long as you possibly can.*

Before going ahead with a patent application you are strongly advised to carry out a thorough patent search (Chapter 1), otherwise you could just be throwing money away attempting to patent an unoriginal idea. If you did a search some time ago, do it again to cover more recent applications.

Then write to the Patent Office for application forms (see **Useful addresses**). They'll also send two very helpful free booklets, Patent Protection and How to Prepare a UK Patent Application. After reading them, decide whether to tackle the paperwork yourself or employ a patent agent. When the official forms arrive, the stages of application are:

❶ You or your agent must prepare a description of your invention highlighting the novel features for which you want a patent. Send it, with the official fee, to the Patent Office. This establishes an official priority date.

❷ You have exactly one year from your priority date to decide whether to go ahead with a full application. *The patent system allows this 12-month 'break' precisely so you can find out if your idea really has a commercial future. It's rarely long enough, so don't waste a day of it.* Full application will involve considerable extra costs so you need to be able to justify going ahead.

Ideally, by the end of your year you should have struck a licensing deal with a company which takes care of your patenting costs. In practice you're unlikely to get to such an advanced stage in only a year, which is why the timing of your patent application is so important and why it may be worth considering another option: spending the year laying the foundations of your own business, a process over which you have much more control (see Chapters 13-18).

❸ Within the same 12-month period you must also apply for any foreign patents you think you need. You'll be able to use your UK priority date. BUT: applying for foreign patents will massively increase your costs, so unless you've found a company or backer willing to foot the bill you need *very* strong evidence of (a) originality and (b) excellent commercial prospects before accepting such a large financial risk.

❹ If within the 12-month period you don't request an official search, your application lapses and won't be published. Or you can withdraw it earlier and refile the same application, as long as no one has seen it or your idea except in confidence. *You lose the priority of your previous application, so you're at the back of the queue again - but at least you have a further 12 months to explore commercial possibilities before incurring major patent costs.* Refiling gives you more time to find a backer, but it's risky. If someone else files the same idea after your first priority date but before your second (or third, or fourth. . .), you lose out.

❺ If the search report reveals a ton of prior art, you might want to drop out. If you go ahead, the Patent Office will examine your application in depth. Here you have a choice. The normal procedure takes up to four and a half years, but you can now ask for an accelerated search and examination procedure that *might* get you a patent in as little as a year. It doesn't cost any extra and can help a lot if there is serious commercial interest in your idea. BUT: whereas the normal procedure takes into account rival applications in the system at the same time, the 'fast track' option may miss them; this could cause serious problems later if you get to an advanced stage of development of your idea or product and a strong competing application suddenly leaps out at you.

❻ *Remember that many of the patent system deadlines are absolute and no mercy will be shown if they're missed. Always abide by the deadlines your patent agent gives you, or you may forfeit your rights.*

❼ At the end of it all you may or may not get the patent you want. If the examiners reject some or all of your claims, you could end up without a patent or with one that is of very limited value. Yes, it *is* a gamble.

Foreign patents

International patenting is expensive and complex and *must* be handled by a patent agent. It should be considered only if your invention has clear international implications - a car engine component, for example - and vast financial prospects. *Unless you're already wealthy you should never consider meeting the full cost of international patenting from your own pocket; payment or cost recovery should be built into a licensing agreement.*

The closest you can get to a world patent is a Patent Co-operation Treaty (PCT) application covering over 90 countries. But all this really does is simplify the initial application and delay the need for translation. After that you have to deal with the patent system of each country in which you want to proceed. The PCT application will generally be filed within 12 months of your priority date. It can either be in addition to your UK application or can include the UK as one of the designated countries. Filing a PCT application costs around £2500 (depending on currency fluctuations) plus agents' fees, and provides, at your option, a grace period of either 8 or 18 months before the major costs of proceeding in a number of foreign countries have to be incurred.

In Europe you can now apply for a single European Patent Convention (EPC) patent covering most European states in addition to the UK. But this doesn't help you in other crucial areas, such as North America and the Far East. Initial EPC application fees are currently about £1000, and the total charges to grant around £3000. This however excludes translation and agents' fees, both of which will add considerably to the final cost.

Patenting in the USA

Patent systems and patent law tend to be pretty much the same the world over, but US patent law differs significantly from the norm. Non-US inventors need to be aware of these differences, as a US patent application may be essential for an idea that could sell well in the States.

First, a point that has ramifications whether or not you apply for a US patent:

- Unlike practice in most countries, a US patent application is not published 18 months after filing; it is only published at grant. Worse, no information at all is available about it before grant. In other words, a competing product and patent may spring out at you fully fledged with no prior warning and after years of development. Even if that doesn't happen, non-publication can make life difficult in two ways. First, it creates a permanent danger zone when you're searching for prior art; it may be there all right, but undetectable. Second, if a competitor's patent has not been published in the USA, it is dangerous to assume that there is no infringement risk in the USA; in all probability the US patent is simply in the pipeline awaiting grant.

Then the plus points:

- An inventor can file a valid patent application up to one year after 'going public' with the invention (publicizing it, marketing it etc). This contrasts with the UK and Europe, where you must file before disclosing and commit yourself to a quit-or-gamble decision exactly a year later. In this respect US patent law is much more helpful to inventors; it gives them valuable extra time and freedom to explore commercial possibilities before having to clamber on to the patenting roller-coaster.

- US patent procedure is more flexible than UK or European procedure. You can abandon a US application and have a second bite at the cherry by filing a 'continuation' application with the filing date of your original application. Or if you want to add more technical detail, you can file a 'continuation in part' application, containing both the original and the additional information. Neither manoeuvre is allowed in the UK or Europe.

(For UK inventors, these two considerable advantages beg an interesting question: how about developing your idea entirely in the USA? Given the right conditions - lots of money, good contacts and an ability to control events thousands of miles away spring to mind - it might be worth a try.)

Then the minus points:

- A US patent may be invalid if the applicant behaves 'improperly' - for example by not naming the correct inventor(s), not revealing all the relevant prior art he or she knows of, or not describing the 'best mode' of operating the invention. Although this requirement's higher aim is to discourage attempts to suppress or misrepresent relevant information, at street level it benefits competitors or predators by giving them an opportunity to overturn your US patent. A successful challenge would be doubly catastrophic: your ability to exploit the US market would be severely reduced, and your doubtless large expenditure on US patenting would have been in vain. The best defence, of course, is to make absolutely sure that you behave 'properly'.

- If you and another inventor independently emerge with the same or a similar invention at about the same time, the winner in most countries is whoever files the first patent application. But in the USA, you only win if you can prove you 'made the invention' first. This may sound fairer, but in practice it involves a complicated and expensive legal proceeding called an 'interference' to determine who invented first. *The standard of proof is high and non-US parties are often at a disadvantage because they rarely keep records to the extremely strict requirements of US law.* For example, you must record what you do in bound notebooks with no missing pages and no alterations, and entries must be corroborated and signed within a few days by someone who is not directly connected with the idea but can understand how it works. The general drift is to prevent the fiddling of evidence, but sticking to all the requirements is a tall order for the average inventor. *If this is likely to be an area of concern to you, contact a UK or US patent agent for a full and current list of requirements and advice on how to implement them.*

Above all, non-US citizens should never embark on a US patent application without specialist advice. In the UK this normally involves your UK patent agent liaising with a US patent attorney. Patenting and selling in the USA carries a lot of risk because the USA is a deeply litigious society in which many lawyers operate on 'no win, no fee' terms. Someone may therefore challenge your patent or product on the flimsiest grounds if they have nothing to lose and much to gain.

Finally, a repeat warning about commercial invention agencies. Several questionable US or US-based companies (some have satellite operations in Britain, Ireland and Europe) advertise widely in UK newspapers and magazines for inventions and product ideas. The pitch can be highly professional, but be under no illusions: they are after your money, and lots of it. You may be tempted by their promises to protect your idea in the USA; but although they may lodge papers for you at the US Patent Office, *that doesn't amount to a patent application.* Despite the best endeavours of the US trading authorities, who fine or shut down the worst offenders, they have a remarkable talent for surviving and even flourishing. We don't want to condemn all US invention agencies as a rare few are capable of reasonable work, but in practice it may not be worth trying to sort the good from the bad; both the chance and the cost of getting it wrong are too high.

Legal costs insurance

Specialist insurance policies may cover your legal expenses if you have a good case against an infringer, or if your right to your intellectual property is challenged. Premiums can however be high; ask a patent agent for details and advice. Separate policies cover patents, registered designs, trade marks and copyright. They're essentially to help you defend a strong position, but won't cover you if your case is too weak or if you just want to harass blameless competitors.

Insurance has obvious benefits if you're marketing your own product, and can be helpful when negotiating with potential licensees: however, *any disclosure that you're covered by insurance may invalidate the policy,* so check its terms carefully.

Chapter 7
Benefits of licensing

Why license your idea to a company?

Successful exploitation of an invention requires three kinds of ability:

❶ Inventive or creative ability to provide opportunities or solve problems.

❷ Skill and experience to 'package' and communicate the idea's potential to others.

❸ Single-minded entrepreneurial drive to get the product on to the market.

Few inventors have all three. A very few may have all the skills but not all the time or all the money. One solution is to team up with others who have those skills and start a business, an option covered later. Another is to license your invention to one or more companies, and that's the route we're going to explore in the next few chapters.

If you have skills 1 and 2, you're probably capable of going the whole distance yourself. If you only have skill 1 (you may not recognize this unless someone tells you!), you probably need either an associate or a representative with skill 2.

For many inventors, therefore, licensing is the route to take: not because it necessarily offers better prospects of getting the product to market (it often doesn't), but because it offers the lowest personal risk. And as with the business start-up route, reducing your risk has to be your priority at all times.

What is a licence?

A licence is permission granted by you and backed by the law which allows someone to exploit intellectual property which the law recognises as belonging to you. In plain terms it allows you to sub-let your intellectual property for an agreed period to someone other than you (usually a company) who can do what you can't - namely, manufacture and market a product made from your idea. In broad terms a licence:

- Protects you by making the company reward you for the use of your idea.
- Protects the company by preventing you from then selling your idea to others (unless the licence specifically allows this).
- Enables either of you to take action against others who steal or copy the idea.

Ownership

It's vital to note that *if there is more than one owner of an idea, all must agree to the granting of a licence.* Without such agreement, all you can do as a part-owner is make the product yourself, which can be limiting if not impossible. You might think it would be in everyone's interest to agree to a licence, but that frequently isn't the case. Hidden agendas and power games bedevil many business ventures, and there is no lack of examples of exciting innovations that suffered needless delay - or never made it - because of an intransigent co-owner.

Why should companies be receptive?

Since most companies can't themselves originate all the ideas they need to stay in business, it's highly likely that they'll periodically look outside. It's often said that an ingrained 'not invented here' attitude makes companies hostile to external inventions, but if such an attitude ever was widespread, few can afford to display it now. (We suspect that some inventors find it easier to blame the 'not invented here syndrome' rather than accept that nobody actually wants their ideas.)

There may be a lack of enthusiasm in companies with R&D people whose careers depend on their ability to come up with new ideas, but few companies can now finance much in-house R&D. Most are increasingly ready to look outside, even if that normally means licensing in existing products from other companies - though there's no reason why this shouldn't include your own business if you start one or form a joint venture! (Chapters 13 onwards.)

Because it's a duty of management to use company resources to maximize the potential of the business (that is, increase its value), acquiring and exploiting intellectual property ought to be an important part of corporate strategy for companies of all sizes. Studying markets, assessing new ideas and looking for reduced-risk, potentially profitable opportunities are now - or should be - key management tasks if companies want to remain competitive.

Advantages of licensing

In general, *licensing in* allows companies to take advantage of other people's initiative and enterprise without imposing unnecessary risks and development costs on the business. It can boost company performance significantly, by:

- Enabling more efficient use of company resources.
- Providing access to new, proven technologies.
- Extending the company's market.

A company's own products or technologies can also be *licensed out*, an objective which may be worth building into your strategy if you want to start your own business but don't want to 'grow' it beyond a certain level. Benefits can include:

- Easy entry to new markets (including overseas) via companies with experience of those markets.
- Ability to meet market demand where the company's own resources can't cope.
- Resolving potential infringement problems. Granting a licence to a company itching to copy-cat your product may have cost-saving and profit-boosting advantages for both of you.

Cross-licensing is another possibility. This allows two companies to make and sell each other's products without fear of infringement problems. They only work if both companies are equally energetic about marketing the licensed-in product, so you need to take care that your deal isn't in practice so one-sided that you're giving away much more than you gain.

When to license

Many inventions are suitable either for licensing or business start-up - which can include joint venture - and the final choice may depend largely on your circumstances and preferences. Some inventions however may be much better licensed, including:

- 'Add-on' inventions dependent on an existing product (for example an improved cooling system for a particular make of electric motor). These are often best licensed to the manufacturer or supplier of the host product.
- Products which require high and unavoidable equipment and set-up costs, such as chemical engineering, major DIY or consumer electronics (where a good example is the Dolby noise reduction system).

Other inventions may fare better as business start-ups than licensed products. These can include:

- Products in fragmented 'expertise' industries where small players can thrive: for example software or specialised instrumentation.
- Cheap-to-make products which depend primarily on marketing, where there are usually several ways to minimize, reduce or defer costs.
- 'Conviction' products where an individual (an inventor or entrepreneur) is confident that a product will succeed, or succeed better, if marketed in a particular way that companies are unwilling or unable to try.

What can be licensed?

Any intellectual property or legally recognized rights that give you an edge over the competition, including:

- Know-how or confidential information.
- Copyright works.
- Shapes and patterns.
- Patents for inventions or improvements.
- Trade and service marks.

It's vital when trying to reach an agreement with a company to remember the range of things that can be included. It's quite possible to have a blockbuster agreement that includes a separate licence - and thus a separate royalty - for all of the above. Never assume that a licence for (say) a patent renders other elements unimportant or unsaleable. *If you limit yourself to patents and exclude everything else, your licensing agreement may be devalued or even worthless.* This is because it's impossible to predict how the different components of your intellectal property might change in value over time. The best example of this is trade marks belonging to successful brands.

When the companies which own them are sold, the price frequently far exceeds the value of physical assets such as buildings, land and equipment.

Excluding any valid intellectual property from your licence agreement could eventually cost you a fortune, so don't be tempted or cajoled into leaving out 'minor details'.

Chapter 8
Selecting companies to approach

Is your idea ready to present?

Before approaching any company you need to be confident that you have enough credible market research evidence to make the commercial case for your product and enough technical evidence to prove that it is better and/or cheaper to manufacture than competing products. Your blood pressure may rise with impatience and frustration, but never present your idea prematurely. You have more to lose than gain.

In particular, a working prototype must work properly. Companies don't expect perfection but they'll be unimpressed by an idea that needs a lot more work even to get the prototype right. They'll focus not on what your product could do but on what it does do, which is not much. We've witnessed several dire presentations where prototypes not only failed to work but were clearly incapable of ever working without total redesign.

Match the company to your product

- Don't approach companies with no experience of your target market or without the equipment or expertise to handle your product. You shouldn't, for example, approach a metal fabricator with an idea that needs plastic injection moulding.

- Be cautious about approaching large companies if your forecast of annual sales is low relative to their turnover.

One inventor's small domestic appliance was turned down by a company grossing over £100 million because they judged it would sell 'only' 250,000 units a year. It found a home with a smaller firm for whom it was manna from heaven. (This illustrates the Achilles' heel of some large companies when it comes to innovation: the sales level at which a product becomes worthwhile is often so high that they can't afford to dabble in many new products.)

- Be equally cautious about very small companies, who might find it difficult to increase production or invest in improved facilities if sales sky-rocket. (Though you and they might, as discussed in the last chapter, be able jointly to license the product out.)

In general you need to look for companies of the right size to whom you can hold out the prospect of either larger market share or a strengthened product range. Your ideal company is likely to be in the small to medium-sized sector and a player in your target market. It may have either a relatively small market share and a strong wish to grab more that could be granted by your product, or a gap in its product range that your product could fill perfectly. It may also be a supplier to one of the market leaders - usually a much better route to major league success than approaching market leaders directly (see Treat market leaders with caution below).

Identifying prospects

If you wish, you can leave prospect identification to professional technology transfer agents (ask your local Business Link for help in contacting them: see **Useful addresses**). This will however cost you some profit, so we assume you'll prefer to do it yourself, at least initially.

From your market research you should have a pretty good idea of the companies operating in your target market, and roughly how they rank in terms of market share, size and turnover. If you don't know who they are, consult trade directories - first try the excellent Kompass directory found in most libraries - for details of significant UK companies and their products. For local prospects you could try asking a Business Link or Chamber of Commerce. Although there are many thousands of companies in the UK alone, after analysing the information available about them your real choice of worthwhile firms to approach will rarely be greater than a hundred or so for a low technology product, and could shrink to a scant handful for an extremely specialized idea.

The fewer companies there are to approach, the better your product and presentation have to be because the risk of 100 per cent rejection is that much higher. If that happens but your faith in your idea is undiminished, you may want to think seriously about starting your own business venture, dealt with elsewhere in this book.

One company, or more?

Depending on the nature of your product, you may need a parallel strategy for selecting companies. Most inventors dream of one large company offering them a licensing package that leaves them with nothing to do except collect royalties. It can and does happen, but profound changes over recent years in production and marketing practice tend to make that ideal less achievable.

In most industry sectors companies are becoming smaller and more specialised, with large companies tending to become clusters of smaller, autonomous divisions. Other downsizing practices include buying in products and services from other companies, or franchising to independent operators. These tactics spread the trading risk and protect the core business if markets suddenly contract.

All this fragmentation and laying-off of risk tends to make a single all-encompassing licensing deal harder to get. A licensing agreement remains the best option for most inventors, but to steer your product to market within a reasonable time-scale you may also have to play at least a partial entrepreneurial role.

You may find that some companies will want to sell your product but not manufacture it, while manufacturing companies may only be tempted if they get firm orders from retailers or distributors. If you can't find one company capable of doing both, you may have to find two or more: one willing to manufacture, at least one other willing to buy.

If you have to choose, *go for companies that sell rather than manufacture.* If you get firm orders at the right price, it should be relatively easy to bring a manufacturer into the fold. Going to manufacturing companies first is likely to be less rewarding if they're used to responding only to firm orders which you can't give them.

Treat market leaders with caution

Don't run straight to the market leaders, the handful of companies dominating a particular market. This advice goes against the instincts of many inventors, whose first and often only thought is of the blue-chip names and the huge markets they command, so here's the justification:

❶ Most big companies are reluctant to deal with inexperienced and under-financed inventors; it's too much trouble and the risk of being let down is high.

❷ They'll be financially committed to existing products

and processes, and the cost of changing to something different is likely to exceed any gain. Your idea may have to be in the astounding league before it crosses their viability threshold.

❸ The bigger they are, the more complex and long-term will be their market plans. Your idea may not fit in, no matter how good it is.

❹ If your idea would replace one of their existing products that is selling so strongly that there's no reason to drop it, you may be harming yourself and an eventual licensee by giving early warning of competition.

❺ Their R&D personnel will easily understand your idea, so what if they reject it then launch something remarkably similar? It may be coincidence, but showing them your idea is risky if you have no way of finding out what they were working on at the time. (In this context, going to smaller companies may be less of a risk if only because most can't afford their own R&D resources!)

❻ Market leaders receive many unsolicited ideas. Because most will be worthless or irrelevant, they may end up on the desk of someone who can only glance briefly at each and would sooner be doing something else anyway. Unless your idea is very well presented or has an exceptional benefit that leaps out, rejection may be a foregone conclusion.

❼ You may have to wait a long time for a response. If time isn't on your side - for example if you've filed a patent application - you can't afford undue delay. Even if the company shows an interest, they may drag their feet for months then drop the idea. *Remember that time is far more important to you than it is to them.*

❽ Many large companies only look at ideas protected by at least a patent application. If you haven't already filed, the cost and time implications of patenting may make it unwise to accept assessment on those terms.

❾ Some market leaders may not look at *any* unsolicited ideas, knowing that many will be similar and fearing legal problems if they accept one and reject another that isn't much different. For safety and convenience they often prefer to buy ideas from specialist product development companies - so find out who they are and approach them instead! (But don't confuse such companies with invention agencies, who often describe themselves as 'product developers'. The genuine ones won't want any payment unless and until they succeed in placing your product with one of their client companies, and even then their reward typically takes the form of a split royalty agreement.)

It may be that in the long run the clout of a market leader will give you the fortune you're looking for. If your product sells well with a smaller company they'll probably want to capitalize on its success as much as you do and a tripartite deal with one of the majors might then be more realisable. But when you're in a hurry to secure an income-generating licensing deal before your idea eats you out of house and home, starting with market leaders can be hazardous. If you insist on approaching them - and some inventors do get lucky, despite everything we've said - you must cover your gamble by approaching other companies at the same time.

Checking out companies

At some stage you'll need to check out companies who respond, as you may have a few sharks in your net. Make all the effort you reasonably can to establish their commercial and legal status, their track record and whether or not they're solvent. (Many libraries keep databases of company information; to go deeper, use company search or credit investigation services.) Is it likely that they have the capacity to exploit your invention? What's their record of dealing with other people and other businesses? Do any of the directors have a history of insolvency or worse? Could they just be after your money, or after grant money with your idea as bait?

The less scrupulous they are, the keener and more willing to please they may seem. It's a shame to have to be so suspicious, but the effort of checking companies thoroughly is amply justified by the appalling experiences of many unwary inventors and start-up entrepreneurs.

Chapter 9
The initial approach

Contacting companies

Often, the hardest part of dealing with companies is getting them to take notice of you at all. The following suggestions may help when you start contacting companies to tell them about your invention:

- Subject to adequate protection, if you have something worthwhile to talk about or show - especially trial batches of product - a good strategy for winkling out company or investment interest for relatively little effort is to promote your product through a press release. Even a short paragraph in the right periodical may yield a handsome return in enquiries, often from totally unsuspected sources. See Chapter 17 for more details. (One of the authors did just this for a small company launched to sell a DIY product. In five years of approaching companies directly they had sold a total of 1000 units. A short press release aimed at trade periodicals resulted in sales of a further 1000 units in less than a month, and sales have continued to climb following further very low-cost promotions.)

- Don't waste time and money phoning companies except to find out who best to write to. It helps to address a named individual, but finding the right person can be a problem in larger firms. Ask the switchboard operator for help. Say: 'I want to send details about a new product that might interest your company, but I don't know any names. Who's the best person to write to?' If you're transferred higher up the ladder, sound businesslike and try to give subtle reassurance that you're not going to be a pest. In passing, confirm the address; businesses move or re-arrange themselves surprisingly often.

- If in doubt, target the marketing director rather than the technical director. The former is more likely to see opportunities for profit in your idea; the latter is more likely to see problems that he doesn't want to know about. In the case of smaller companies - many of whom don't have marketing specialists - mail to the managing director.

- Prepare a brief summary of your idea - *less than one side of typed A4.* Don't disclose more detail than is needed to convey its key marketing, technical and financial benefits. Use plain English and plain facts, arranged as bullet-points or numbered lists for clarity and brevity. Don't boast or make wild claims. Include your name and contact details. Attach a diagram or photograph if necessary, but don't go overboard. Your aim is to whet their appetite, not provide them with so much detail that they don't need you.

- You can mention that your idea is protected by patent application *but as long as it remains unpublished, don't disclose any detail that isn't in the public domain: in particular, don't show drafts or copies of the application.* Refusal may require tact if they're not to dismiss you as crankily secretive, but the fact is that your application is privileged information until it is published; at this stage the less they know about your protection the better.

- Send a copy of the summary to each company on your list, with a short covering letter along these lines:

Dear [name],

I enclose brief details of my [name of product] which is available for license and may be of interest to your company. A working prototype is available which I shall be delighted to demonstrate to you subject to suitable mutual assurances regarding confidentiality. (Also enclosed is a copy of a confidentiality agreement which I hope you may be able to sign.)

I can attend a meeting at fairly short notice. If you need any further information, please contact me. I look forward to hearing from you.

Yours sincerely. . .

Hints, tips and cunning wheezes

- *Don't call yourself an inventor,* even if it's obvious that you are. It's not a word that opens doors. Present yourself as a business-minded individual with a sound proposition to make to fellow professionals. The fact that it involves a new product is incidental. (And call it a product, idea or innovation but *not* an invention.)

- After a week or so - when your contact has had time to decide how to react - make a follow-up phone call to find out how your idea has been received and to press your request for a meeting. Take rejection as breezily as you can, listen hard and ask questions (including 'Where did I go wrong?' Disarming frankness rarely goes totally unrewarded). You may learn things that help improve your approach to another company, or even to the same company later on. Always try to gain something, even if it's just an invitation to re-pitch if you improve the idea or think of others.

- You may even be able to reverse a rejection by countering objections - which despite your best efforts may be based on a misreading of your idea - as long as you don't do it confrontationally. ('I take your point, but what about. . .' beats 'You've got it all wrong'.) After all, the best salespeople frequently close deals where lesser mortals take 'no' for an answer.

- When you ring most large companies, the person you want invariably isn't available. Keep ringing until they are available rather than leave your number and wait till hell freezes over for a return call.

- If you get written replies, don't be fooled by flattery. If they say your idea is 'most interesting' or 'ingenious' but there's no offer of a meeting, it means they're not interested but haven't forgotten how to be polite. Equally final is the letter saying your idea 'does not at present fit in with our plans'. A genuinely helpful letter gives it to you straight: 'It's wrong for us because of this and this'. You can learn from letters like that.

- A get-rid-quick tactic sometimes used against totally dud ideas is to praise the invention, then innocently ask the inventor to solve 'just one small problem'. The problem is of course large and unsolvable. (A similar letter might tell you that the company genuinely thinks your idea needs more work or some other input - such as approval by a safety body - before they'll look at it, but the difference in intent should be clear.)

- Unless you have a patent application, try to get the company to sign a confidentiality agreement (see Chapter 6) before any meeting. If they refuse, as many large companies will, your choice is to trust them - which you usually can, at least at this level - or look elsewhere. If offers of meetings are not thick on the ground it's probably worth the risk.

- If you get an appointment, confirm the date and time in writing. *You may be allotted less than half an hour in a busy diary, so aim to complete your 'act' in 10-15 minutes.* If your prototype has a long operating cycle, or has to be demonstrated outdoors, or has any other special requirements, mention this in your one-page summary and give the company written notice well in advance so suitable arrangements can be made. Make sure everything is fully set up before you 'perform'.
- Strictly for your own use in meetings, prepare an information file that you can dip into for answers to questions. Make sure it's easy to use and that you know what is and isn't in it. You don't want to 'die' looking vainly for the answer to a perfectly reasonable question.
- Returning to an earlier point: *don't discuss or carry with you anything related to the technical or claims content of your patent application.* The point is that your prototype won't embody all possible variations of your idea but your unpublished patent application(s) might. To hinder any attempt to steal your idea by varying it, you need to keep others in the dark about how many variations you yourself have spotted and protected.
- Never try to explain your product without a prototype, *but don't rely on the prototype alone to persuade people.* They'll want convincing facts and figures, and they'll be reacting to *you*: are you the sort of person they could sensibly do business with?
- Treat your encounter as a friendly meeting of equals, not an appearance before a judging panel. The fact that they've let you in at all shows a degree of curiosity that you can exploit. Take brief notes (including the names and job titles of everyone at the meeting), ask shrewd questions, and try to assess them as individuals. Could you do business with them? As a professional touch

(and to stop them forgetting you too quickly) hand out business cards. Straight after the meeting, scribble a quick report of what happened and what action, if any, was promised. Also record your perception of the attitudes of the people you met; identify the one who is likely to be your best advocate within the company.

- If the meeting isn't going your way, don't despair. Listen and learn. If they know their market well, you'll pick up some gems of information.

- After the meeting, write to thank them and to confirm any outcomes. It's both a courtesy and a precaution, as your letter documents your understanding of any agreed actions. If your understanding is wrong, they should write back to correct you. If they don't, and promised actions don't materialize, your letter makes it harder for them to back-pedal later.

- If they reject your idea, *insist that they confirm in writing that they have no further interest in pursuing it.* They're then less likely to be tempted to develop a similar product later and protect their rears by claiming that they hadn't *actually* rejected your idea.

- As a general rule confirm back to them in writing all significant verbal undertakings given to you, particularly when they involve numbers - money, percentages, key dates etc - and keep copies of all inward and outward correspondence. (We can't recommend taping phone conversations as it may be illegal, but it isn't difficult. . .) *This is as much part of your protection as a patent application, so make the effort.* It's not unknown for some companies - and, it has to be said, some inventors - to move goal-posts quite blatantly if they think they can get away with it.

Chapter 10
Assessment by companies

What must companies look for?

Understanding how companies have to look at new ideas is an important part of the battle to win them over - or more accurately, to get yourself accepted. They ideally want an idea that will give them a mountainous profit for no risk. They know they're unlikely to get it, but that's the direction they'll be coming from. Not in a million years will they look at your idea and say: 'Hey, this is so good we must do it, no matter what it costs us!' Before taking any risk involving a substantial commitment of funds or time, a company must be satisfied that everything about your idea stacks up. The key factors they'll look at are:

- **The product**
  Does it fit in with the company's marketing and production strategy? Are the necessary resources available? How much more development will it need? (Almost certainly far more than you think. Feel the temperature plunge as you airily suggest that your idea 'just needs a few minor problems ironing out'.) What quality standards must it meet? etc.

- **The intellectual property**
  How extensive and valuable is it? Patent application notwithstanding, is the idea original *now*, let alone after a possibly lengthy period of development? Is the protection strong enough to resist circumvention or challenge? Who will own, pay for and protect the patent? Will the inventor's know-how be available?

- **The market**
  Is the market ready? What's the sales potential? What's the right price? What's the best launch strategy? How much may have to be spent on marketing and promotion? How are competitors likely to react? How are distributors, retailers and especially the company's own sales team likely to react?

- **The inventor**
  Is the inventor an asset or a liability? Does he or she behave sufficiently professionally to enable both sides to make reasonable progress towards a licensing agreement? If not, is the product outstanding enough to make the pain worthwhile?

- **The cost**
  Is the project affordable, and how is the money to be raised?

- **Risk versus return**
  Is the project a significant risk to the whole business? How soon will the product recoup costs and go into profit? How long is the profit likely to be sustained? If the product takes the company into unfamiliar territory, how are shareholders, investors and the bank likely to react? (In some larger companies, keeping twitchy shareholders from baling out or demanding heads on spikes is virtually the only thing that drives senior executives.)

If this list seems to duplicate tasks we advise you to carry out (particularly patent searching), don't think that lets you off the hook. Duplicate with a will. Different people rarely approach tasks in exactly the same way, and it can only be to your mutual advantage to compare results and methods and identify where either of you might have gone wrong.

In general, these points are worth emphasizing when you strike up an initial relationship with a company interested in at least assessing your idea:

- Companies have very limited freedom to act on impulse; they must carry out a full cost and risk analysis (a process known as 'due diligence') before committing themselves to any significant new idea.

- Post-assessment rejection doesn't necessarily mean a company thinks your idea won't succeed, but it does mean they think it isn't right for them. It's difficult for this kind of decision to be reached entirely objectively, so the more positive evidence you can present or (particularly when it's a small company) the more input you can offer to make a development project succeed, the more you may be able to influence the verdict.

- *Don't sit back and expect companies to do everything right.* They're not infallible and smaller firms may not be much more experienced at innovation than you. Plenty of companies don't do their homework and launch products that sail straight into a sea of grief. You could face large problems if you're tied by a licensing agreement to a company badly holed by your idea, so your own research efforts may be essential not just to further your own interests but to help the company as well.

- For best results even with large companies, be prepared to offer or accept some kind of joint venture opportunity (see Chapter 14). It shows a 'can-do' attitude and will win you more points than if you just sit there and expect the company to do everything.

Prototype assessment

Expect interested companies to want to keep your prototype for a period of detailed assessment. This is where you can come unstuck, especially if you only have one prototype.

If you've filed a patent application, the clock is ticking away and your idea needs to be considered by as many companies as possible in that time. You certainly don't want it locked inside one company for months. It's hard to meet both your own and a company's needs with a single prototype, but these guidelines may help you to juggle more effectively:

- Don't leave a prototype behind at first visit. Tell the company you'll gladly let them assess it *subject to a written agreement on conditions of loan.* Don't release your prototype until you get something in writing signed by a manager with appropriate authority. It needn't be a long or complex document but it should cover clearly and unambiguously most of the issues in this list. If the company won't co-operate, go elsewhere rather than cave in. The prototype is your property and you have a right to keep it in your full control.
- Establish what they physically want to do with your prototype, and who will be responsible for its safe keeping. Will they pay for immediate repair or replacement in the event of loss or avoidable damage? (You could try charging an appropriate deposit. You'll get a mixed response to this, so explain clearly that you're only doing it as a form of insurance.)
- Negotiate for the shortest reasonable loan period and *insist on a specific end date.* If their interest seems lukewarm and there's a risk your prototype might end up on a low-priority slush pile, don't release it for more than ten or so working days. (They can always ask for a

second loan later.) Include in your *written* agreement a date and time when you'll turn up and collect it.

- A month is ample for most initial assessments. *Don't loan your prototype for much longer without some form of payment.* **This is important.** Without that spur a company may hang on to it indefinitely and most likely forget about it or even lose it.

- The more the company wants things its own way - for example long and exclusive assessment rights, barring you from even talking to other companies - then (1) the more they must pay for their privileges and (2) the more essential is a formal written contract. This should ideally be drafted for you by a patent agent, as some companies will renege without a blush if the wording is so loose that they don't feel legally threatened. (So will some inventors, but that's another story.)

- Most companies won't want to pay, so be ready for a battle of wills. If you feel out of your depth let someone suitably qualified negotiate for you, but don't lose sight of the fact that a rapid Yes or No decision is equally important, so bid for a speedy outcome as well as cash.

- How much the company should pay depends on the potential value of the product (see Chapter 12). It should be enough both to recompense you for not approaching their rivals and to stir them into brisk action. *If the terms offered are derisory or if they refuse to pay anything, walk away.* A possible exception is if there are potential deferred benefits - for example if it's a small company with a keen interest but no spare cash, or if the company guarantees to research the market or make samples which are yours if they drop out.

- Payment in instalments is more acceptable to companies than a lump sum, so ask for (say) £750 a month for as long as they keep your prototype beyond 30-40 days, or for as long as they hold you to a sole rights agreement. Make it clear in your contract that (1) if they haven't given you a firm decision by the time the agreed loan period ends, their sole rights lapse and you're free to approach other companies; and (2) if an instalment fails to materialize when due, the deal is immediately void.

- Payment should also contribute towards the upkeep of your idea during the loan period. The most significant cost may be patenting; if you've got by up to now on confidentiality agreements alone, you may need a patent application before releasing your prototype. Assessment unavoidably reveals your product to other people, and once you leave the one-to-one arena of first meetings a confidentiality agreement ceases to be worth much.

  There are two options: the more likely is that you pay for patenting and build as much of the cost as you can into your loan period payment. Less likely, as it requires an almost instant commitment to your idea, is that the company pays directly. They may want co-ownership of the patent, but this may be a price worth paying if it lifts a large financial burden from you. *A patent agent's advice will however be essential, and you must insist on continuous proof that the company is doing everything correctly and on time; the patent process keeps strict deadlines and any delay or omission can be fatal.*

- Finally, *never pay for assessment no matter how it may be justified* - for materials, research, compliance testing etc. Someone is simply after your money. Reputable companies wouldn't dream of it, but we've heard of others who suggest that paying them for an assessment grants you access to major companies with whom they have a relationship. Don't believe it for a second.

Chapter 11
Reaching agreement

The art and craftiness of negotiation

The stage where you and the company sit down and start hammering out a royalty agreement is from your point of view the most important part of the whole relationship. We look at actual figures in the next chapter; the purpose of this one is to equip you for the process of negotiation itself.

Asking and being asked for money is a fraught affair at the best of times, and relations between inventors and companies can easily turn sour if one or (in the case of many smaller companies) neither side has any previous experience of negotiating a royalty agreement. Problems seem most likely to occur when the idea has been with the company for a long time, during which (a) the issue of money has been delicately avoided and (b) as with most lengthy relationships, the initial fizz has gone.

Avoiding conflict

You and the company will of course have been talking since you first met, but over time the relationship may have changed in subtle ways that only now become apparent. To head off a clash across the negotiating table, look out for the following signs that may herald conflict:

- The company starts to think it's more their idea than yours - and they may be right if they've done a lot of expensive development work on it.

- The other side of the same coin: you think total credit for the idea should be yours, and don't fully appreciate what the company has done to improve it.
- They start feeding you gloomier sales forecasts as launch date and the cold reality of selling a new product (and paying you a royalty) approaches.
- Your perception of your idea (world beater) seems to be starkly different from theirs (okay, but nothing to go wild about).
- The technical or marketing people with whom you've built a rapport are suddenly replaced by accountants who just want to get rid of you as quickly and cheaply as possible.
- You find that what you thought were shared beliefs and expectations are now held by you alone. History has been rewritten, goal-posts moved. (That's one of the reasons why it's a smart move to keep copious records of all dealings with companies.)
- *Often - very often - the inventor is too demanding or inflexible.* This one at least you may be able to do something about.

While all companies will seek a licensing agreement weighted entirely in their favour, few actually expect to get it; they'll compromise to some extent and will expect you to do the same. Many inventors on the other hand expect their every demand to be met in full and are affronted when offered far less. Negotiation quickly degrades into conflict, then deadlock, then a sticky bog of mutual recrimination.

There can be dangerous consequences if a company feels that an inventor has unreasonably refused a fair offer; it may justifiably threaten legal action to recover development or other costs already incurred.

(In passing, one case where this happened illustrates the perils of partnerships. The product - a good one with exceptional royalty potential - had two inventors. One was happy to accept the deal offered by the company, but the other was greedy; he started making impossible demands and broke faith repeatedly during talks lasting a year. The company finally ended negotiations and started legal action to recover more than £50,000 it claimed had been spent on development. It had no choice but to sue both inventors jointly.)

The object of negotiation

Read this carefully and memorize it:

> **The object of negotiation is not to win. The object of negotiation is to reach agreement.**

This is enormously important. If one side wins the other loses, and that's a recipe for long-term problems as the loser tries to regain ground at every chance. Thus, if you negotiate for a win it's probable that neither side will end up happy.

Once you get close to a licensing deal you will usually be involved in two rounds of negotiation, each leading to the signing of an agreement. The first level is :

Heads of agreement

This is where both sides sit down and thrash out the basics, trying to find as much common ground as possible. The aim is to identify the figures, terms and conditions that both sides are broadly happy with, enshrine them in a preliminary document called *heads of agreement*, then hand that over to lawyers to be rewritten as a full agreement in dense legalese. With some exceptions - see **Professional help** later - heads of agreement discussions usually work best without formalities or the potentially inhibiting presence of legal representatives. It's therefore perfectly acceptable to conduct your own negotiations as long as something positive is emerging.

Important: Heads of agreement are generally 'subject to formal contract', a term with much the same meaning as the 'SOLD subject to contract' sign on a house: it's sold only as long as neither side pulls out. *So even if everything goes swimmingly, it's vital that you don't let the company go ahead with the project until the heads have been written up into a full agreement.* The danger is again much the same as handing a buyer the keys to your house before you've got his or her money.

If the company adopts a resolute 'take it or leave it' stance you should either walk away or immediately seek the professional advice of a patent agent or solicitor, not least to assess whether the deal is worth making at all. You must however enter negotiations knowing broadly what kind of a deal you want, and be prepared to disclose your stance judiciously as talks progress. As in a card game, all players need to be seen sticking to the cards they've got and can't suddenly produce extra aces from a hidden deck.

What are you negotiating about? The following model of what can be included in a heads of agreement document gives you some idea of the issues that must be tackled and resolved in order to reach a workable agreement, initially in broad terms but later in copious legal detail. *Its range is typical but by no means complete; ask a patent agent or solicitor to advise you on additional aspects specific to your idea which may need to be tabled for discussion.*

❶ **Heading**

HEADS OF AGREEMENT
Subject to formal agreement

❷ **The parties**
Name, address and status of the proposed 'Licensor'
Name, address and status of the proposed 'Licensee'.

❸ **An introduction**
For example: These Heads of Agreement contain a record of preliminary negotiations between the parties to a proposed licensing agreement. Their content is not legally binding until a formal contract has been executed.

❹ **Intention**
A basic expression of what the agreement is about, covering:

- *What is being licensed*
  A descriptive title of your invention/product and list of all the intellectual property on offer (including official numbers where applicable): patents, trade marks, registered designs, copyrights, know-how etc.
- *What the licensee intends*
  He/she wishes to exploit the invention in a particular territory and requests that the licensor grant a licence to manufacture and sell the product(s) with the use of defined intellectual property.

❺ **The licence**
- *Level of exclusivity*
  Basic variants are:
  - *Exclusive:* only the licensee can manufacture. This may be insisted on if the product involves significant expense, lead-time or promotion.
  - *Sole:* only the licensee and licensor can manufacture.

  - *Non-exclusive:* allows several licences and is typically best for add-ons in competitive sectors (for example the Dolby noise reduction system).
  - *Semi-exclusive:* by territory, type of industry, application or time.
  - *Assignment:* a special case where the licensee takes over the patents and other intellectual property completely.

- *Territory*
  The country or countries to be covered by the licence. If there is a long lead-time or high investment the licensee will want to insist on worldwide territory, though you can't restrict activity in countries in which you have no legal protection (unless your licence is dependent on non-territorial intellectual property such as know-how).

- *The market*
  May be defined/limited by type of industry or application. (You may be able to grant several licences for different markets, thus increasing total market penetration and royalty levels.)

❻ Payment

- *Basic royalty rate(s)*
  Including reducing percentage with increased turnover. See Chapter 12.

- *Some guarantee of payment*
  To stop the licensee just sitting on the idea (see Chapter 12). You may have to agree to any 'overpayment' in the early, poor years being clawed back in later, better years.

- *Advance lump-sum payment*
  You'll be extremely lucky to get one (see Chapter 12), but if you have costly patents to support, try to

get those costs covered in the licence. You're in a stronger position for such payment if you have know-how or other vital documentation to be handed over on signing. (You should never, of course, reveal the contents of such documents before getting the agreement - and the money - you want!)

❼ **Confidentiality**
Always include a standard confidentiality clause, whether or not you already have a separate confidentiality agreement, as it forces the licensee to safeguard anything you disclose.

❽ **Duration**
Usually the lifetime of the last patent but sometimes (and better for you) a short term - typically one to five years - with renewal options. That makes it easier for you to end a poorly-performing licence. It can be difficult to prove poor performance quickly, so always include a *termination clause*. The simplest is failure to meet agreed minimum royalty levels, as this is hard for the licensee to dispute.

❾ **Things to look out for**
These are potential minefields, so beware!

- *Who owns improvements?*
  The licensee may develop the technology over time, or apply it to different products. Who owns the improvements - you or him? He may justifiably object to paying you a royalty for his improvements. Try to extend the licence to cover improvements, or at the very least insist that your royalty doesn't drop if the licensee improves the product.

- *What if your patents are successfully challenged?*
  It may pay you to specify what portion of the royalty is associated with which elements of intellectual property: for example 50 per cent to

patents, 25 per cent to trade marks and 25 per cent to know-how. That way, even if you lose all patent cover you'll still get something. Or you might specify lower levels of royalty, duration and guaranteed payment if patent protection is lost.

- *Who challenges infringers, and who pays?*
  It's dangerous to accept responsibility unless you're rich. Far better to leave it to the licensee and accept a lower royalty for shedding the risk. Don't rely on legal costs insurance (Chapter 6); it only works when the insurers expect you to win, and some inventors are notorious for groundless legal challenges.
- *Infringement of third-party intellectual property rights*
  Never give any warranties that your invention does not infringe other people's intellectual property rights. This is akin to handing your licensee a loaded gun to point at your head.
- *Manipulation of value of sales*
  You must limit the licensee's scope for declaring an artificially low value of sales. He will justifiably want the value to be net of all deductions, but these can be legion and at the shady end can include 'sweetheart' deals whereby he sells product at an unrealistically low price to friends or associates. To avoid this, specify *arm's length transactions*; this enables a court to arbitrate.

⑩ **Standard clauses**
A whole pile can be included, most of which either clarify detail such as when and how royalty payments will be made, access to accounts for verification and how disputes will be arbitrated, or cover important but unlikely points such as termination (see ❽), how to ensure acceptable standards of product in the event of termination, and permission to sub-licence.

Always ask 'What if?' questions

Expect all the above elements to be present in some form or other in your agreement. Make sure that every point you can think of is covered and try to work out exactly what each one means to your future. Ask yourself 'what if?' questions for everything. If the answer is unsatisfactory or you don't understand it, renegotiate until that point is clear and acceptable. It won't always be in your favour - remember what we said earlier about the purpose of negotiation being not to win but to reach agreement!

It may help to have your own heads of agreement drafted out in full before the meeting. Don't slap it on the table as a fait accompli as you stand to lose too much face if the company rejects it clause by clause, as they will certainly try to do; but it can be useful as a frame of reference to help you gauge whether you're gaining or losing ground if the going starts to get confusing. (Exceptions are if you're in such an immensely strong position that you can call all the shots, or if the company produces its own ready-written heads of agreement and expects you to sign it. We've never heard of the first happening, and if the second happens you may have a bare-knuckle fight on your hands from the very start and may need urgent professional advice.)

Full agreement

If you've gone through the heads of agreement stage and are happy that they're acceptable, the next stage is to convert them into a full legal agreement. (You don't have to go through the heads of agreement stage. In theory you can go straight to a full agreement, but in practice this is rare.) The full agreement will inevitably be a complex and near-incomprehensible document, often of scores of pages, which neither you nor the company's negotiators will be competent to draft. This is a job for legal specialists, though you will be consulted on points of detail; the company will use its own advisers, so you must use your own patent agent and/or solicitor to make sure that the final document is consistent with the heads of agreement and doesn't contain hidden traps not imagined when drawing up the heads.

Don't look on the full agreement as an opportunity to undo the deal. Best policy is simply to say to your legal adviser: 'Here's the outline agreement; I'm happy with the terms and figures, so please draft a full agreement based on them.' Unless your adviser finds evidence that something is badly wrong or unworkable, or spots a way of improving the deal for everyone, resist any offer or temptation to renegotiate by the back door. Maybe you were steam-rollered here and there, but the die must now be regarded as cast and any eleventh-hour intervention is more likely to wreck the deal than improve it. In any case, most professionals charge by the hour, so any intervention that delays conclusion of the agreement may cost you money as well as lose you goodwill.

Tips on negotiation

Few of us are born negotiators, but research published in 1989 by the Huthwaite Research Group identified these acquirable traits that distinguish skilled negotiators from the average:

- **They spend more time asking questions**
  This gives them more control over the discussion by reducing the other side's thinking time. A question is also more acceptable than naked disagreement: 'Are you really sure about that?' beats 'I think you're wrong'.
- **They spend more time summarizing what has been agreed**
  Their aim is a workable agreement based on shared understanding. Average negotiators tend to be keener

to reach a rapid agreement than to spell things out and risk more wrangling.

- **They're much more likely to signal their behaviour**
  For example, prefacing a query with 'May I ask a question?' This is better at forcing a response; it also slows negotiations down, reducing combative tension.
- **They say fewer favourable things about themselves**
  They avoid references to, for example, 'our generous/reasonable/fair offer', knowing that they serve no useful purpose and irritate the other side by implying that they are ungenerous, unreasonable or unfair.
- **They keep their cool**
  Once tempers start to fray, negotiations often enter a rising spiral of attack and defence. Skilled negotiators spend less time attacking and defending, because both modes are generally aggressive.
- **They make fewer counter-proposals**
  Ping-pong matches of proposal and counter-proposal bog negotiations down.
- **They use fewer reasons to back up their arguments**
  That's because as more reasons are wheeled out, more points become available for disagreement. A good negotiator omits weaker reasons, knowing they will become the focus of the other side's attack.

Negotiating abilities

In general, to be a good negotiator on your own behalf you need four key abilities:

- To keep a clear view of the outcome you want.
- To understand the other side's position.
- To foster trust by displaying integrity.
- *To know when to get up and walk away.*

Knowing when to say 'enough is enough' is important because not all negotiations end satisfactorily, and as long as you're confident that your demands are not unreasonable it's safer to pull out than accept a bad deal. That way you still have an opportunity to seek a better deal with another company.

Negotiations are always psychologically complex. At stake is not just money but relationships and personal goals. It's important to gauge how well you get on with the company on a human level, because if the chemistry isn't right the negotiations are unlikely to go well. *If there is no rapport or trust, your first and most important decision may have to be whether to stay or go.* There may for example be a 'killer' on the company team - someone who doesn't like your product and raises objection after objection. If that individual holds sway over the others it may be better to tackle him or her head on and courteously but firmly indicate that you'll leave rather than waste time fighting. That puts you in control, if only for the time it takes you to reach the door. On the other hand it could be just the firm gesture needed to clear the air and get the talks back on track. Whatever you do, do it decisively and with all the self-confidence you can muster.

Finally, and perhaps chiefly, *you must be prepared to be flexible.* There's no point clinging to a totally fixed position if the company can't afford even to get close to it. Time, percentages, fixed sums and rights are almost infinitely variable, so with mutual goodwill it should be possible to reach an acceptable overall agreement by making a series of compromises, some favouring one side, some the other. Remember that in business there are usually many different ways to arrive at the bottom line you want; *everything* is negotiable. (To put it another way: if the cake is well and truly cut up and your slice won't get any bigger, remember that cakes come in a box. Why not ask for the box . . ?)

Professional help

If you're confident that your product has real international potential we recommend that you involve your patent agent, solicitor or other professional adviser in all discussions *including heads of agreement*, as you'll be out of your depth attempting to negotiate licences covering several countries and perhaps involving overseas companies. If prospects are so good, hang the expense; this is a case where the cost of *not* having professional support could be vast.

If negotiations take place entirely overseas it may be tempting to use professional services based in that country, but beware. It's difficult to check quality or performance and in many countries, especially the USA, it can be virtually impossible for a non-national to sue for malpractice or incompetence. Many UK patent firms have agencies in or professional links with other countries, so you're likely to be safer leaving everything in the hands of your current patent agent.

Irrespective of your product's potential, if you so seriously doubt your negotiating ability that you don't want to be directly involved in any discussions, not even heads of agreement, you can assign front-line duties to someone else with appropriate competence. A patent agent is once again probably best, as much of the discussion will centre on intellectual property. Your patent agent will in any case be involved in drafting the full agreement, so there is sense and some economy in having him or her at the table from the start. Anyone else - a friend with business experience for example - will need at the very least some knowledge of intellectual property law, the judgement to decide what is in your best interests, and an ability to get on well with and earn the respect of the company side. People like that are not thick on the ground.

Chapter 12
Working out royalties

How much do you deserve?

Your financial expectations must be realistic; if you insist on too high a royalty, negotiations with a company are likely to get nowhere. Before starting heads of agreement talks you must find out what is an acceptable ball-park percentage for a product like yours, then try to attach a floor and ceiling to your negotiating position. The floor is the percentage below which you do not drop unless desperate. The ceiling is the maximum you feel you can justifiably ask for without making the company think you're too greedy or naive.

Ideally, both sides have roughly the same figures in mind and are happy to meet somewhere in the middle. *If you and the company find that your respective floors and ceilings are several storeys apart, check your own figures and assumptions and, if possible, theirs too. If you still think you're right and you can't convince them, it may not be worth even attempting to reach an agreement with that company.*

We'll now explain how to arrive at figures you can sensibly discuss, but we must stress that the 'typical' percentages used as examples may be invalid in your case. The scale of your reward *in percentage terms* depends largely on three variables:

❶ **What's your contribution to the product?**
If all you've really done is give the company an idea which they've turned into a product through extensive redesign and development, and especially if they're also

paying upkeep costs such as patenting, you can't expect much of a royalty - perhaps less than one per cent. But if you've done the lion's share of development and given the company a near-perfected product, you deserve a larger than average percentage. (NB: whatever you may have spent on your idea prior to approaching the company will not normally count as 'contribution'.)

❷ **How special is the product?**
If it has to be keenly priced to compete with other products performing similar tasks, the company's profit margin will be low and so will your royalty percentage. But if the product is so special that there is little or no competition, the company can charge whatever the market will bear. The higher profit margin should justify an above-average royalty percentage for as long as the product dominates its market.

❸ **In what volume will the product sell?**
The more units sold, the lower will be the royalty percentage you can expect. This may sound perverse, but it reflects commercial reality. Profit margins shrink as customers place larger orders but insist on lower prices, yet manufacturers may at the same time have to invest more in production resources. Why should they give you a bigger share of the profit as their risk rises but yours doesn't? The perfectly correct view held universally by astute businesses is that even at a lower percentage your income will rise considerably if they sell a lot more. So don't complain - be grateful. *For a product estimated to sell in boatloads you might be offered a fraction of one per cent, but it could still make you a multi-millionaire.*

Before asking for anything you should try to locate your product on these three scales, then average them out. It's bound to be a hazy calculation, but it may help you to gauge whether the figures proposed by the company are a downright insult or merely on the low side of realistic.

Many inventors who don't go through this process of adjusting their expectations in line with reality make the mistake of equating a low percentage with low income. The size of the percentage ultimately doesn't matter that much; what matters is the size of your bank balance. The lesson is that while you should certainly push for the highest realistic percentage you can get, you mustn't lose sight of the fact that a tiny share of huge sales can make you a lot richer than a large share of meagre sales.

Calculating royalty rates

Most royalties are expressed as a percentage of the product's *net sales price* - that is, the company's selling price minus all taxes and other less obvious losses such as returns, samples, pilferage, damage, degradation etc. But although it's an easy calculation to make and subsequently verify once the product is up and selling, it won't help you establish the **value** of the product for negotiating purposes. *Net sales price therefore gives no indication of the royalty percentage you should get.*

A solution is to calculate your opening royalty bid on your estimate of the product's likely *gross profit per unit and probable market size*, as both are relatively easy to estimate and a much better indicator of value.

Basically, the bigger the potential gross profit per unit, the better should be your prospects of negotiating a high royalty. For example: if your product can be made for a penny and sold for a pound, there is far more profit and thus more scope for a high royalty than if it costs 50 pence to make but still can't sell for more than a pound.

Calculating gross profit is simply a matter of deducting from the selling price the cost of manufacture. If you don't already know the production cost you can find it out by asking manufacturers for quotations based on the sales volume forecast by the company. *If the company can't or won't tell you their sales forecast for the product or its proposed selling price, pack up and leave now as meaningful negotiation will be impossible.*

Next estimate the size of the probable annual market for your product, as that's another factor that determines its value. A product that can potentially sell in huge numbers for at least several years has a higher value than a product with the same gross profit per unit but only a limited life in a small market.

Note that probable year-on-year market size isn't the same as the company's sales forecast. The latter will be much lower, partly out of sensible caution and partly to stop you getting ideas above your station. That leads to another not necessarily obvious observation: your royalty should apply to *all* sales, whether or not they exceed the sales forecast. Unless it's part of a package offering the option of a substantial guaranteed minimum royalty income (see **Advance payments** later), *never accept a royalty agreement that stops paying out once a stated level of sales is reached.*

(We've heard of grumbles within one major company to the effect that a certain well-known inventor has earned far too much in royalties. As the product in question has almost certainly boosted that company's turnover by hundreds of millions of pounds over the years, such an attitude would be pretty dumb.)

Once you've estimated gross profit per unit on forecast sales and have a clear notion of your product's overall value, don't bid for too high a share of gross profit. The company's eventual net profit will be much lower, so a demand for a large (say 50 per cent) share of gross profit will be refused point blank. Your best shot is likely to be between 10 and 25 per cent of gross profit per unit.

For guidance, this table of typical profit margins and royalty ranges was produced in 1993 by the University of Edinburgh's UnivEd Technologies Ltd. Note that these are *maximum* royalty ranges; as we've said, *actual* percentages can be subject to a great deal of usually downward variation.

Sector	Gross profit *as % of total sales*	Max royalty *as % of net sales price*
Primary industries	10-20	2-5
Industrial intermediates	20-30	3-6
Consumer durables	30-40	4-7
Consumer non-durables	40-50	5-10
High technology products	50-60	7-15

(Primary industries produce raw materials: steel, oil, chemicals etc. Intermediates are materials, process machinery etc for use by other companies. High technology products are generally specialized and not mass-produced.)

If you're puzzled by the discrepancy between the royalty percentages in the table and our statement that 'Your best shot is likely to be between 10 and 25 per cent. . .', bear in mind that your royalty is a percentage of a percentage. To illustrate: if a company makes a 20 per cent gross profit on its total sales, 10-25 per cent *of that 20 per cent* gives you an eventual maximum royalty of 2-5 per cent of net sales price.

In our experience 2-7 per cent of net sales price is the range within which most royalties fall, though that shouldn't stop you aiming higher. The two per cent end is for products selling in large quantities (typically hundreds of thousands); the seven per cent end for those selling at more modest levels (typically tens of thousands). Four to seven per cent for an 'average' product is good going, while some specialized products such as software or medical equipment should exceed 10 per cent without too much trouble. *Very few companies make net profits of over 10 per cent, so to get a decent share of that is a considerable achievement.*

A worthwhile refinement is to accept or even suggest a sliding scale of royalties based on the total royalty income involved. For example: 7 per cent up to £20,000-worth of royalties, reducing to 5 per cent between £20-50,000 and to 3 per cent when your total royalty income exceeds £50,000. This shows that you acknowledge the company's falling profit per unit as sales rise and demonstrates your professionalism and your willingness to be flexible in everyone's best interests.

Advance payments

The hefty advance payment that many inventors think they should automatically get is in fact extremely rare, and for good reason. No matter how much you may have spent on your invention, it's likely to be tiny compared to the sum the company must raise and gamble on the success of your product, and that may take years to recoup. Therefore, unless your invention is very special, there is little hope of a sizeable advance lump sum. Smaller companies in particular often have such limited financial resources that a large money gift is simply out of the question.

Company accountants will in any case resist a large early payment on the grounds that the effects of interest rates and inflation make it more expensive than paying the same sum in instalments over two or three years.

A more realistic way of getting payments in advance of sales is to negotiate a guaranteed minimum monthly or annual income. Once sales exceed the level that sum represents, you get royalties as well. This would normally take effect from the date production begins, but if that's likely to be a long way off it's reasonable to ask for a guaranteed income starting now, but perhaps deductible from future royalties.

Ask for this minimum to be a small proportion - 25-30 per cent - of projected annual sales. If you've broadly agreed a royalty of 2 per cent on projected sales of 500,000 units at £4 net sales price, your income should be £40,000. At least 25 per cent of that - £10,000 or about £830 a month - is the sort of pre-production income you can justifiably ask for. To some extent you're challenging the company to put its money where its mouth is and that may make them uncomfortable, but if they suddenly have to revise their selling ability downwards by 75 per cent - which in effect is what they'd be doing if they said they couldn't afford such a sum - then perhaps they shouldn't be in business.

If sales remain as forecast for some years, your royalties will soon recoup even several years of advance royalties. *The shorter your product's likely commercial life, the more important it is that you receive guaranteed payments.*

Fixed-sum payments in lieu of royalties

A company may be delighted to offer a fixed sum instead of royalties if they think that in the long term the idea will make them a fortune. Smell a faint rat if such an offer comes your way, as it could be a ploy to buy you out for peanuts. On the other hand it could backfire on the company. An inventor we know was offered a choice of £1,000,000 outright or 3 per cent royalties with a guaranteed minimum of £60,000 a year. He chose the latter, estimating a £200,000-plus annual royalty, but at the time of writing - four years later - sales show no sign of reaching even the minimum royalty level; the trend, if anything, is downwards.

Moral: if the bribe is big enough, take it seriously.

Beware fiddled sales figures

Finally, two warnings:

❶ **Never agree to royalties based solely on profit**
Sales figures can easily be manipulated to show no profit at all, and with a little ingenuity almost anything can be deducted from profit as a business cost. Even tax inspectors have a hard time here, so you won't stand a chance of disputing the company's figures.

❷ **Make sure the company sells the product fairly**
A manœuvre beloved of some companies is to sell at an artificially low price to one of their own divisions or to an associate company in order to deprive you of your full due. This can be hard to detect, so to avoid it insist on *arm's length transactions* in your final agreement (see Chapter 11). Then if the company does pull a fast one, a court will adjudicate on the basis that it should have sold at a fair price.

Chapter 13
Starting your own business

What if you can't get a deal from any company?

You can give up, or you can *consider* starting your own business.

We stress 'consider' because most people aren't cut out to run a business and there are many risks even for those who are. Self-employment can be liberating, but it has serious drawbacks too: if you really want to change status from solid citizen to dodgy credit risk, becoming your own boss is one of the fastest ways of doing it.

Starting your own business - or becoming an entrepreneur - to get a truly promising new product to market should be seen as a positive option, not a last resort. *Nor need it mean abandoning your goal of a licensing deal with a company.* It can simply mean going out into the market and doing enough to be able to go back to companies later with evidence that your product really does sell.

There are plenty of books on business start-up, so there's no point duplicating them here. From our experience only three things really matter: one is knowing at all times where you stand financially; the others are getting customers and getting paid, and there's no guaranteed way of doing either. The rest is detail you can easily pick up as you go along.

What we want to dwell on is **how to survive**, as that has to be your absolute priority. All small businesses are at risk in their start-up phase; new small businesses based on innovations even more so. The following bits of miscellaneous wisdom have been collected from successful entrepreneurs whose businesses all had modest beginnings. We hope they help.

Limit your risk

Entrepreneurs are often hailed as risk-takers. In fact, good entrepreneurs limit their risk as much as they can. In particular they create escape routes so they can exit fast if things go wrong. In the words of one, who started his engineering business in a hen shed and is now a multi-millionaire: 'If you want to be successful you must first avoid failure. You can't hope to get it right if you don't first reduce your chances of getting it wrong.'

Your initial goal should therefore be a cautious one: *to operate a business for only as long as it takes to find out if your product does or does not sell.* You're out to prove a point, not make a profit. If the point turns out to be unprovable you must be able to get out instantly with minimal loss. You should be able to run such a business in your spare time.

Three pre-conditions are important though:

- You must have some grounds to believe your product will sell, despite all the rejections. Does your research satisfy you that it really is better or cheaper than the competition?
- Your product should not be so costly to make or market that it requires levels of finance no one will give you.
- You must be clear about your motivation and goals, as in business the roles of technical innovator and entrepreneur often clash. (As one company owner put it: 'Brilliant inventors are prone to announcing Mark II before you've actually sold any of Mark I.')

Minimize your start-up costs

Work from home if you possibly can. Many successful businesses start in spare bedrooms, holes under staircases, attics and sheds. Apart from keeping reasonably warm and dry, the simple ability to communicate with people is half the battle, so all you need is a phone, answering machine, fax and ideally an entry-level business computer system with a printer so you can produce letters and documents of acceptable quality. You also need letterheads which double as invoices, printed with an appropriate name style or logo (which is usually worth having professionally designed).

If you have workshop facilities at home, keep them for testing or demonstrating your product. *Unless your product gives you very high profits at very low volume, you won't have time to do your own manufacturing. Your main role will be to mastermind sales and marketing while other businesses literally produce the goods.*

Subcontract manufacture

It makes no sense to set up production facilities from scratch when you can subcontract to existing businesses looking for work. Take time to find the right one and don't let price be your only consideration. You might find a small cheap company but can they produce the right quality? Could they meet rising demand for your product? Can they be relied on to despatch orders straight to your customers? Can they extend you any credit? A bigger, more expensive company may be an all-round better bet as long as they don't give you second-class treatment when it suits them.

If your product has several components you may need more than one subcontractor. This raises some problems, but overcoming them is what being an entrepreneur is all about.

- Every part must fit, so you must provide each subcontractor with absolutely precise specifications. If you don't exercise strict quality control you risk being stuck with unsaleable product that has to be either expensively reworked, or scrapped and remade.
- You must find subcontractors of matching performance or the whole operation will drop to the level of the least efficient.
- You have to juggle everybody's payments and credit terms.
- You may have to set up a separate assembly operation, possibly including packing and distribution. This gives you total control over the finished product but may mean laying out cash for premises and labour.

Premises

Never buy. Rent by the week or month and look not necessarily for the lowest rent but the least tying tenancy agreement. Look also for problems that may be costly to live with. For example if offered a large cheap space, think of winter; if an upper storey, think of vehicle access; if a ground floor, think of break-ins. Ask other businesses if they have spare space to rent; they may be grateful for the money and more flexible than a formal landlord, and may allow you access to other facilities. Don't think of image (yet) because that's always expensive and may anger investors. Buy equipment and fittings cheaply, for example at auction.

Stay in day-by-day control

You must know how your business is running all the time: whether you're profitable or not and especially whether your cash flow (money coming in minus money going out) is positive or negative. *Cash flow determines the health of your bank account and is always more important than profit.* Don't be squeamish about harrying slow payers, and always be ready to sacrifice some profit to maximize your cash flow. For example, pay suppliers by the longest payment option but offer customers discounts for prompt payment - making sure that any agreement on payment terms is written into the deal at the outset, as it will be difficult or impossible to put in place later. Be constantly alert for any threat to your cash flow: for example from rising sales, which may deplete your cash reserves faster than they can replenished from income, especially if you have too many slow-paying customers.

Make your costs dependent on sales

The more you can make your costs dependent on sales, the better. Then, if you only sell half of what you expected, it only costs you half. Some of your costs may rise, for example through placing only small orders with suppliers, but you'll be limiting your risk and that's more important.

Be wary of banks

An overdraft facility should *only* be used to cover temporary cash flow fluctuations. *You should never regard it as permanent borrowing.* Overdrafts are repayable on demand and it isn't unknown for banks to wait until a business pays in a large enough cheque to clear the overdraft, then cancel the facility without warning. That can and often does destroy perfectly healthy firms overnight. Banks aren't 'people' businesses any more; today's bank managers rarely look further than their computer screens, and inexperience of business makes them almost eager to interpret a temporary dip in your trading as a signal to cut you adrift. The all-smiling, all-knowing bank manager who really understands small firms and their problems probably now exists only in TV ads, so keep your bank's hold over your business - through overdrafts, loans, even direct debits - to an absolute minimum. (More than one seasoned entrepreneur told us he'd sooner seek a loan from wealthy acquaintances at over-the-odds rates than borrow from a bank.)

VAT, book-keeping and accountants

It can be worth registering for VAT even if you're trading below the compulsory registration level, as it may be difficult to compete if you're not registered but your suppliers and business customers are. Inability to pass on VAT raises your selling price or forces you to cut your profit margin. Other benefits: VAT registration gives you the status of a 'proper' business, and paying VAT means your books are never a mess for longer than three months. *You must however be genuinely trading*: Customs & Excise won't enjoy sending you regular cheques. They're also much more vicious than Inland Revenue and can hit you very hard if you break the rules.

Even a tiny business can generate a lot of paperwork, so it may pay to hire a freelance bookkeeper for a few hours a month to take care of your books and VAT; they're usually much cheaper than accountants, whom you should use only to work out your tax at year-end or to advise on specific tax-related or financial problems.

Project planning: time and cost forecasting

There's always a big difference between how long a project - in your case, getting a business off the ground - should last and how long it actually does. To get somewhere close, multiply all time calculations by three. There's no rational basis for this formula except that it works more often than not. Time stretches and all sorts of things can become dislocated as you deal with people who don't share your burning desire to get a result. It's important to be aware of this and take steps to ensure that extra time doesn't cost you serious extra money. For example: don't print brochures too far ahead of need; so many details may change in the meantime that when the time comes, you can't use them.

Choose your customers with care

Lots of small customers is good because it spreads your risk even if it increases your administrative chores. Or concentrate on 'blue chip' customers - large reputable companies or public sector organizations. Treat large orders from small businesses with caution. Many are only a prayer away from insolvency; moreover, an unscrupulous owner won't limit the size of his order if he knows he isn't going to pay. Always insist on a written order, and if in doubt insist also on a large enough deposit to cover at least your material or subcontracted costs.

A common sting is the order placed by company A to supply major company B. You think you're safe because company B is a respected name *but your contract isn't with them.* Company B pays company A; if company A then doesn't pay you, you lose. If the order is big enough to threaten your business, insist on payment with order or at least a large deposit. Alternatively, put the boot on the other foot: offer to supply company B direct and give company A a cut. If they won't play ball, refuse the order.

If the order will take a long time to fulfil, ask for stage payments and stop the job dead if an instalment doesn't materialize on the agreed date. Never overstock on verbal assurances that a large order is imminent. (In fact, don't overstock or over-produce at all; try to maintain just enough stock or production to keep pace with demand.)

Getting paid

If you can get away with it, insist on payment with order. A big problem for most businesses is slow payment; 30-45 days from good payers, 60-120 days from the majority. Add the time taken to fulfil the order and you can be looking at six months from start to finish. Everyone moans but to no effect, as most businesses are caught in the same vicious circle. *If yours isn't a cash with order business you must take this into account when preparing your business plan, as it may mean no income at all for a large chunk of your first year.*

If it all starts going wrong

If your venture is clearly failing, it's vital to act quickly to limit the damage. Having a shoe-string business designed to be shut down rapidly obviously helps, but failure leaves most businesses saddled with at least some debt. Talk immediately to key creditors, including suppliers, before they start pursuing you. Early warning gives everyone a chance to sort something out and stop your business failure - an unremarkable event in itself - from turning into a personal disaster, especially perhaps for friends who have backed you with their cash.

Chapter 14
Joint ventures

The partnership option

What if you've done the rounds of companies and no one has shown any interest in licensing, but you're convinced that your best long-term plan is still to place your product with a company? There is an additional option to starting your own business, and that's a joint venture or business partnership with someone with the expertise and resources that you need. That 'someone' is most likely to be a company, but it needn't always be.

It could be another individual if they have strengths where you're weak: money, technical or marketing expertise, a business track-record etc. Or it could be a university, as most now have business units looking for opportunities to exploit commercially their own research or specialized resources. If your product has sufficient profit and innovation potential and their expertise can help get it to market, they may be interested in a joint venture. Different universities have different technology interests and areas of special (often world-class) expertise, so you may have to shop around.

Let's assume though that your joint venture will be with another company. It could be with a large company willing to fund or in other ways help you to develop your idea further so that they have a better idea of its potential. This might look like an opportunity to grab with both hands, but the danger is that the larger the company, the less commitment there may be to your idea. At the end of the project they may not see enough profit potential in their terms to want to market your product, leaving you with the problem of what to do next.

Smaller companies may offer better prospects. A small company may like your idea but be reluctant to take the plunge into full commitment. The problem for the average small firm is the cost and time involved in developing and marketing a new product. Marketing may in fact be outside their experience if their main business is supplying other companies. But assuming they like your idea enough to commit some resources to it, your willingness to lighten their load could be exactly what is needed to start the ball rolling. For example, to market your idea they might have to employ someone and thus add an extra salary to their payroll. If you do the marketing, they may save thousands of pounds immediately.

To borrow an apt phrase from the context of Hollywood film-making: *If you want to succeed, don't offer people problems; bring them solutions.*

From the company's point of view a joint venture can be a cost-effective way of getting something done quickly or getting a share of serious potential business at low risk to themselves. *If such an opportunity presents itself, take it very seriously.* The typical inventor's objection is that the company will get too big a share of the cake, but that fails to take into account the reality that serious company involvement can dramatically increase the size of the cake and at the same time reduce the inventor's exposure to risk.

If the company, the inventor and the idea are all compatible, a joint venture strategy makes business sense as it isn't far removed from the conventional practice of farming development and marketing work out to specialists rather than doing it more expensively or less well in-house. Many small to medium-sized companies have experience of starting or buying into smaller companies to explore new avenues, and may have a strong enough innovation philosophy to overcome the usual aversion to dealing with inventors.

Regrettably, in most instances we know about the inventor has let the company down, by missing deadlines, overspending or veering away from the agreed plan of action.

If offered this kind of opportunity it's vital that you meet agreed time and cost targets *even if your best guesses turn out to be wrong and you make no money from the exercise.* At stake are both your credibility and your product. In business terms you're simply a supplier and don't deserve any special favours, though the unusual circumstances may in practice win you some latitude. Flag problems as you see them coming and if you can't solve them yourself, ask the company for advice. A good company will read that as a positive sign and won't knowingly let you flounder. At a push you might get some extra time, but don't expect any extra money unless something happens that neither of you could have foreseen.

Meeting companies half way

What you don't want in any joint venture is a totally one-sided situation where the company can't lose but you can. If your business venture is in effect arm's length R&D for a specific company, they should be prepared to support you in some significant way - for example by letting you use their equipment and premises (a big saving to you that may cost them little or nothing) or giving you a budget to buy materials or a 'consultancy fee' to stop you starving.

Do not however expect to walk in off the street and in five minutes persuade a company to become a partner in business.

You must have skills and abilities they recognize, and a commitment to your idea that they can respect. You must come across as a disciplined professional with clear and achievable aims, and not as just another chancer. *(You might in fact already work for them.* A joint venture can be a good way to benefit from an idea that is intellectually yours but belongs legally to your employer, especially if he or she can't otherwise do much with your idea except sit on it.)

You should both agree achievable goals and deadlines, including a system of reporting progress and dealing with problems. You should draw up a joint contract to take care of sticky details like who owns (or owes) what in a myriad of eventualities: if you fall out, if you or they go bust, if your business turns into a gold mine etc.

You must also sort out exactly how much control you have. Are you really your own boss or just a risk-bearing dogsbody? For example, the company might want to assign someone to assist you. This can be an asset if they have expertise you need, but a danger if they learn everything about your part of the business or if their authority overrides yours. Even if the company is genuinely trying to do you a good turn, control could drift away if you're not strong enough to draw a clear line and keep them on the far side of it. Control is vital to any business, so share it only if the risk is fairly shared. *And make sure that if the company fails to keep its side of the bargain, you have the right to pull your idea out - improvements and all, even if these eventually have to be paid for - so you can continue trying to market it.*

This is an area where problems need dealing with quickly before they get out of hand, so you need a patent agent or solicitor 'on tap'. You should in any case seek professional advice at initial agreement stage, and certainly before signing anything or allowing any work to begin.

Chapter 15
Business plan

Who needs a business plan?

You must prepare a business plan if you want investment, grant funding or a significant borrowing requirement for your new business. *Its primary beneficiary though is you. You're the one who most needs it, to prove the viability of your idea and to guide your progress.* A business plan turns vague optimism into firm predictions and inescapable detail, and helps reduce early risk by enabling you or others to spot potential problems and deal with them.

Its main uses are:

- To record and justify your assumptions.
- To enable others to examine those assumptions.
- To test the reality of the claimed market opportunity.
- To make sure nothing has been overlooked.
- To help you and others track progress.

Business plans are often disparaged for being little more than 'future fiction', and many seasoned investors look primarily at only one thing: the skills and experience of management. (See ❼ below.) One way to counteract a lack of relevant experience is to update your business plan every month or even every week, replacing guesswork with hard fact as events unfold. It may be a chore, but you'll win valuable respect for making the effort to maintain an accurate and honest account of your situation.

There are no rigid rules on how to construct a business plan (though grant applications may have a required format). Essentially, it should be clear and brief and contain the following elements:

❶ **An executive summary**
No more than one side of A4 outlining:
- Who you are: career, qualifications, experience.
- What you want to do.
- Why your product will sell.
- Your existing resources.
- The extra resources your business needs to succeed.

❷ **The business**
Explain your concept. If the business already exists, give its history and current status. Indicate where you want it to be in three to five years' time (the typical span of an investor's desire to be involved).

❸ **The product**
What it is (in *plain* rather than technical language), what its competition is and why your product is better. *Clearly state its advantages.* 'Competition' must include products which do only an approximate job pending the arrival of your innovation. Provide proof of originality and ownership (patent searches, patent applications etc). Detail any need for necessary or desirable further development, including compliance testing.

❹ **Market information**
Indicate what market research you've done to establish sales potential. This should include market size and more detail of competition (selling prices, sales volume etc). List your sources of information. *It isn't enough to say that X million people could use it and if only one per cent buy it you'll be rich.* That was said years ago about

an anti-theft device for a make of computer used by many schools; it turned out that most users *wanted* them stolen so they could replace them with something better! Even highly professional market research can be spectacularly wrong about new products (remember the Sinclair C5?), so if possible include letters of intent, actual orders or even proof of sale of a few prototypes.

❺ **Marketing techniques**

How will you promote and sell the product? To whom and at what price? Forecast your sales *and justify them.* Your cash flow forecast (see ❽) will show if you can afford what you propose.

❻ **Manufacture and distribution**

How, who and where? (Techniques, equipment or resources, capacity, suppliers, subcontractors, labour, premises, location, transport, storage, delivery etc.) If you need to buy equipment, how do you justify a large up-front cost when you can least afford it? How will you control quality and service?

❼ **Management**

What human resources will you need and how will you manage and pay for them? List your own and other available key skills, with full CVs. If your proposed venture is large enough include an organization chart and remuneration policies. Identify missing skills and explain how these gaps will be filled.

❽ **Finance**

First, identify and fully justify what you need to get started, and forecast your profit and cash flow (also known as your operating budget). You must include all costs and the list can be amazingly long. Second, indicate what funds you can provide yourself. Can you get additional unsecured finance, for example grants? Next come the 'What ifs'. These are alternate versions of your cash flow forecast designed to see how much money you might need if your business hit a rough patch on the way to success: for example, if it takes four months to get paid instead of two, or if you only sell half as much as projected in your first year. Something will almost inevitably rock your boat, so this exercise is a worthwhile safeguard. *If you don't do it your potential backers will, and if you give them free rein they'll come up with worse scenarios than you ever dreamt of.*

Lastly: nearly all investors look for exit routes from the start, so indicate how they can get out of your business with a fat profit (as a just reward for their risk) after three to five years.

You may need an accountant's help for all this, but don't ask him or her to bend the figures in your favour; hawk-eyed professional investors won't be fooled.

❾ Risk assessment and future prospects

The main object of a business, especially in its early stages, is to minimize risk. Prove your responsibility by indicating how you'll tread a cautious path. For example, if there's more than one potential market, show that you're aiming for the one that offers least risk. If there's a way to keep set-up costs low until the market is proven, *choose it even if the profit margin is poor.* (Or show how the risk is justified, usually by proving the greater risk of *not* doing it.)

Finally, what if all goes well? How will you cope with rapid growth? This is a barbed question because success is not always a bed of roses. Businesses are at their most vulnerable when growing fast; costs rise, prices may have to rise, and cash-flow may go into reverse as bills need paying faster than cash comes in.

Chapter 16
Raising finance

Reduce the risk to your backers

This is difficult, but the golden rule is: the lower the risk to an investor, the better your chances of getting investment. You and your business plan must convince potential backers that:

1. Your product can succeed.
2. Your business aims are achievable and not pie in the sky.
3. You'll spend their money wisely and sparingly.

High risk is usually associated with a lack of hard information about prospects. You can reduce that risk considerably by having firm orders or letters of intent from customers, and so where possible should try to win orders *even if you haven't yet got a product, or have only a few prototypes to sell.* Evidence of some sales, even if only a handful, is far more reassuring than a glowing report on technical performance but no sales. A potential backer then has at least some information: the product will sell, though how well remains to be seen.

At this stage you won't get any help from banks. They'll never help a high risk start-up unless their lending is guaranteed in full. They only come into the picture once you've got start-up finance from somewhere else and you're trading. But as many small businesses know to their cost, banks are inflexible friends and summary withdrawal of overdraft facilities or recall of loans can be your biggest threat even if you're doing well, so it pays to keep any bank's hold over your finances to an absolute minimum.

Do you really need that much money?

Before looking at sources of finance, it's worth considering whether you really need as much as you think. Some products - in high technology areas especially - unarguably need significant levels of investment or support to get them to market. Many others though depend more for their success on skilful marketing than on costly production, and marketing is an area where there is plenty of scope for trimming and controlling costs. *If you do your own marketing and link it to a strategy of making sales before you manufacture, you may be able to launch your product at a cost you can afford unaided, or that will be much easier to raise from others.*

For example: assuming you have a product poised ready for manufacture, you could for a few hundred pounds mail details of it to a large number of firms. You offer an inducement that makes customers happy to wait for delivery, such as a big discount on bulk purchases made by the end of that month. Then on the first of the following month you instruct your manufacturer to go ahead and produce exactly the volume of product ordered plus a sensible surplus to use as future stock, secure in the knowledge that the money to pay for it all is in the bag. Even if you don't get cash with orders, proof of those orders should make it easier to get extended credit from your manufacturer (especially if he sees good business coming his way from your product) or perhaps a short-term bank loan or overdraft to tide you over until payment starts coming in.

It therefore pays to examine carefully whether you could get by with a relatively small amount to sell *your product rather than a much larger amount to* make *it.* The aim of a business is to make money rather than spend it, so explore every possible way of paring your costs to the bone and wheedling prepayment out of customers before concluding that yes, you do need external finance.

Sources of funding

For an individual prepared to launch a small business venture based on a new product idea the basic sources of funding are:

❶ PERSONAL

- **Family and friends willing to put in small affordable amounts**
- **Small-scale private investors willing to take long shots**
- **Larger scale private investors often known as 'business angels'**

In the earliest, highest-risk stage of commercial development when nothing is known save that there might be a market for the product, you can probably forget all but family and friends. But they can be a potent source of start-up capital, as the inventors of the board game Trivial Pursuit discovered. When every company rejected the idea and they had spent all their own money, they offered $500 and $1000 shares to friends and associates and raised all they needed to launch it themselves. The rest is history. An inventor we know raised £50,000 in lots of £1000 in a few weeks, starting at his local pub. People will often gamble what they judge to be a bearable loss in return for a small but worthwhile stake - for example one per cent per £1000 invested - if the idea appeals and is presented convincingly.

Once you get to private investors it's a much tougher ball-game. Business angels are private individuals with money to invest, usually in the five-figure range that most start-ups need and that is exceptionally hard to find elsewhere. Most are successful business people and professionals who look for three things: effective management, a good product and a worthwhile market *in that order.* If one element isn't up to scratch there might still be a chance. Two down makes it unlikely, so a good product with a small market and an inexperienced inventor at the helm is a poor risk and probably won't be backed. Private investors answerable only to themselves will accept bigger risks than corporate investors, but to stand a reasonable chance of support you must still make every effort to minimize the 'unknowns' associated with your venture.

Private investors often form local syndicates, so find those in your area through a Business Link or from the British Venture Capital Association's directory Sources of business angel capital. Most like to be personally involved in the projects they back (a mixed blessing: some may want to take over entirely if they're unhappy with the way things are going) and usually prefer ventures within easy reach - say less than an hour's drive away.

❷ BUSINESS

- **Potential partners**
- **Joint venture support from a company**

You might find a business partner prepared to invest in your venture, but beware a match so unequal that you risk being sidelined when things take off. A partnership is often a bust-up waiting to happen, so it's vital to have a legal agreement (based on sound professional advice) that defines the relationship and its objectives, the sharing of spoils, what happens if the business or partnership ends, etc.

If you can each invest roughly equally and the division of responsibility is that you manufacture and your partner markets (or vice versa), a possible way of heading off problems is to consider forming two separate businesses: one to manufacture, one to market. You own most of one; your partner owns most of the other. This arrangement protects you if the partnership doesn't work out by enabling you to keep control of the part of the business that concerns you most. Instead of dissolving a business, all you're dissolving is a contract between two businesses.

A company might invest if they're interested in making, selling or using the product themselves, perhaps to secure an advantage over rivals. They may invest not just money but resources and personnel. There are clear advantages in joint ventures (see Chapter 14) but beware giving away more control than the deal is worth. Careful negotiation and a detailed legal agreement will be essential to protect your longer-term interests, especially regarding intellectual property. The advice of a patent agent will be essential.

To repeat advice also given in Chapter 14, if your idea belongs legally to your employer, this type of investment could be a good way for both of you to benefit if your employer is restrained by time rather than money from doing anything with the idea.

❸ PUBLIC FUNDS

- **Government grants**
- **Local and regional enterprise grants**
- **Support from universities**

These sources offer assistance rather than investment, but can help cut your need for investment funding to a level where you're more likely to get it.

The Department of Trade & Industry - acting through regional Government Offices - offers valuable and keenly contested awards to small companies or individuals based in England *

and intent on turning their idea into a business venture, though high technology ideas usually fare best. Individuals may be able to wait until they've got an award before forming a company. Funding is typically a generous percentage of eligible costs (at the time of writing, grants up to £45,000 were available to individuals for feasibility studies into innovative technology). Processing your entry may take some months, but it's a worthwhile wait for the kind of funding that simply isn't available anywhere else.

(* Similar support is provided in Scotland, Wales and Northern Ireland through the Scottish Office Education and Industry Department, the Welsh Office Industry Department and the Northern Ireland Department of Economic Development.)

Contact local authorities to find out what help is available to business start-ups and other forms of enterprise. It varies from area to area, so shop around; it may be worth locating your business away from home *but analyse all grant offers minutely.* Many are repayable if you move out within a stated period (typically three years), during which rents have been known to rise steeply; we know of instances where they became as much as four times more expensive than equivalent premises nearby in the private rented sector. This is just the sort of trap you *must* avoid.

As we mention in Chapter 5, universities are well worth trying as a source of cost-reducing help. Options range from short undergraduate projects in market research, product design or testing (best for individuals) to Government-subsidized schemes designed to encourage academic and commercial partnership on major innovation projects (best for small companies). Most universities now have commercial liaison units; failing that, contact relevant departments direct. Some universities may even take on your idea for a share of the action: see Chapter 14.

❹ VENTURE CAPITAL

- Seedcorn funds
- Venture capital funds

Seedcorn funds are mainly for start-ups launched by experienced managers. Venture capital funds are normally for expansion rather than start-up. Venture capitalists range from big names like 3is (Investors In Industry) to lesser-known regional venture capital groups, some linked to national or local government enterprise initiatives. They usually want to invest at least £250,000 for an annual return of 30 per cent or more, so they'll barely glance at a business like yours, no matter how good the product. What they might do if you get an opportunity and if you strike the right note - both rather large ifs - is point you in more appropriate directions through their network of contacts.

Use of publicity

Innovation prizes - for example the Prince of Wales Award for Innovation - are thin on the ground but give you credibility and should generate interest and enquiries leading to sales, investment or other support, especially if you help the process along by sending out your own press and media releases (see Chapter 17). But beware general publicity in the popular media - particularly TV, where the priority will be to entertain an audience rather than present your product in its best light. Withdraw co-operation if you're being set up as an oddball inventor or if key benefits of your product are misunderstood or ignored, as this is definitely an area where not all publicity is good publicity. (A regional TV programme made a complete hash of one inventor's product, missing its main benefits and enthusing about things he'd told them it *didn't* do. He estimates that in around ninety seconds he lost the equivalent of a year's sales.)

Chapter 17
Low-cost marketing

What is marketing?

Getting your marketing right is every bit as important as getting your product right - perhaps more so, as good marketing can sell a poor product (at least for a while) but a good product won't survive poor marketing.

Many companies rely for their survival almost totally on marketing. By contrast, many others thrive without seeming to do or even think much about marketing. Some dismiss it as expensive froth. They're not good role models for a new business. They've usually evolved a 'blind' marketing strategy that keeps on working for them, but only as long as market conditions don't change much. They often can't see trouble coming, or do anything about it when it hits. The function of good marketing includes looking ahead and plotting a new course if danger looms, or if the old one simply isn't going anywhere any longer.

Definitions of marketing are legion, but in our view and your circumstances it boils down to the art and science of (1) finding and (2) winning as many customers as possible by (3) the cheapest and least time-consuming means so that (4) you can sell your product and avoid going bust.

For a new product the marketing effort divides roughly into two phases. The first is reaching people who *might* buy your product and letting them know it exists. The second is more complicated and involves making your marketing more effective by analysing actual sales patterns: who is (and isn't) buying, and why, and where, and when etc.

You can probably manage at least the first phase unaided, and may have to anyway, as marketing firms are too expensive for most start-ups to contemplate. You'll also have to market continuously, as healthy sales require a sustained marketing effort. *Don't fall into the trap of thinking that if your product is cheap enough it will sell of its own accord.* It won't; and too cheap can mean too little profit to sustain a business.

Effective marketing promotes the benefits of your product that will persuade customers to pay a decent price. It can drive up your price by highlighting the unique selling proposition (USP) or stand-out benefit of your product that its rivals don't have. *This should be your strength.* Many USP claims are hackneyed and unconvincing, but you've got a genuinely new, different and *better* product to shout about.

Marketing is such a huge subject that we can't do more than scratch the surface. What is important is that you study all your marketing options and set your chosen marketing strategy in motion well before Day One of your business.

How do you give yourself a crash course in marketing?

- Many colleges and universities run occasional short, low-cost marketing courses for small businesses, where you can learn and make useful contacts.
- Read: though many books on marketing are too technical for a beginner; look for titles aimed at small businesses. For wit as well as wisdom read books by ad agency gurus who have survived at the sharp end of marketing: for example David Ogilvy's classic Ogilvy on Advertising or Jerry Della Femina's From Those Wonderful Folks Who Gave You Pearl Harbor.

Effective low-cost product promotion

Initially you must look for ways to get free or very cheap promotion and publicity for your business.

The main purpose of promotion and publicity is to generate enquiries for your product in ways that eliminate 'cold calling', which is time-consuming and depressing as the brush-off rate will be close to 100 per cent. (If you still want to try it, get someone else to make the calls; their emotional detachment might improve results.)

Methods of promoting a company and its products include public relations, advertising, mailings and exhibitions, with sales literature (brochures, leaflets etc) as an essential support tool. Forget exhibitions, apart from small local affairs or unless you're offered a cheap share of someone else's stand; they need highly professional handling and are rarely cost-effective at your level of operation. Forget print advertising too, as that eats money and only pays off if ads appear regularly in the right media.

The least expensive method is public relations, which broadly means feeding snippets of information about your company or products to relevant media in the hope that you'll get free editorial coverage. Your initial line of attack should be the press release (or news release if you want to include TV and radio). These are cheap to produce and the required format isn't difficult to master.

Press releases

- **What do you write about?**
  The most obvious topic is the announcement of your new product, but plenty of other subjects constitute news. These include:
  - Product improvements.
  - New product literature.
  - Applications (how customers use your product.)
  - Prizes, awards, major contracts won.
  - Links with other companies or organizations.
  - Information on the business itself (how it was formed, a move to new premises etc).
  - Staff appointments (including your own career change, if significant).

- **Where do you send press releases?**
  To every magazine or newspaper targetted at potential customers - especially trade or professional journals, which often include an enquiry card to make it easy for readers to request more information. Find titles and contact details in British Rate and Data (BRAD) or the more common Willings Press Guide, which is in the reference stock of most libraries. PR Planner is also useful, but harder to find. You may need to write more than one version; trade journals prefer straight technical detail, while local papers will want a strictly local angle with no jargon, some human interest and a punchy first-person quote or two so they can pretend to have interviewed you. Address the editor by name (a worthwhile courtesy) and use a hard-backed envelope if enclosing a photo.

- **How do you maximize your chances of coverage?**
  A photo helps greatly. It should be interesting and of good quality, at least 150mm x 100mm, glossy (to aid reproduction) and ideally in colour. On the back, stuck along one edge with adhesive tape, should be a slip with a caption plus the name and address of your business. Don't use sticky labels or write on the back of the photo.

  Also follow the rules on structure, which are:
  - Head your news item with a relevant and attention-grabbing title.
  - In the first paragraph include your 'news' *and mention your product and its benefits.* Subsequent paragraphs should be in order of importance, as editors chop text from the bottom up; they don't have time to fish out and re-assemble key points. Short releases are thus better than long, so prune out anything irrelevant.
  - Use short sentences and plain English as far as possible, and an appropriate 'voice' (if you produce life-or-death medical equipment don't write as though you're flogging used cars).
  - For releases aimed at local or popular press focus on human interest and include a suitably interesting first-person quote (though if you put words in someone else's mouth, clear it with them first).
  - Produce the release on your normal business letterhead but with the added and clear heading Press Information.
  - Use double spacing with at least a one-inch left-hand margin to allow room to 'sub' the text.
  - At the end put 'For more information contact. . .'.
  - Date the release.
  - To maximize coverage, send releases monthly. If you think hard enough there will usually be something to write about.

- **Monitoring enquiries**
  When each enquiry comes in, log the publication that generated it. You'll gradually learn which work best for you, which can be a good guide to where to place advertising if and when an ad campaign is justified.

Product literature

Most enquirers will want more information. You can do a lot with a standard letter, which is cheap and can be updated easily, but you may eventually need a brochure, leaflet or information pack so:

- If you mail heavily, aim to keep the total weight of your mailing (all enclosures plus envelope, address label etc) to a postage minimum. Better quality paper may add only a few pounds to your print bill, but much more overall if the extra weight nudges your mailing into a higher cost bracket. For further economy choose a size that goes in a standard envelope.
- Think hard about the job you want your literature to do in the hands of a potential customer; it's your 'silent salesman'.
- Keep it simple and *focus on benefits*; avoid extravagant artwork and gushing text.
- Professional input makes a difference (besides print the main elements are graphic design, photography and/or illustration and copywriting) but seek recommendations as quality, performance and price vary a lot. Brief them fully and allow ample time for them to do the job properly and for you to check it.

Chapter 18
Selling

Low-cost or least-effort selling options

If you want to sell your product at the keenest price, with minimal overheads and effort, and without having to give away too much profit to anyone else, these are probably among your best options - though none is without its drawbacks.

- **Mail order**
  Mail order is simple enough in principle: you place an ad in a newspaper or magazine and wait for the cheques to roll in. You get cash up front and can often delay manufacture until you know how much product you need. The drawbacks are the high cost of advertising and the headache of (a) choosing the right publications and (b) creating ads that sell off the page. Don't be tempted to go straight for a big, full-colour splash that you can't afford to run regularly. Modest black-and-white ads with simple artwork can be highly effective, so use them to test the waters.

  There are strict regulations governing mail order ads, so look into them thoroughly first, or publications may refuse your ad. Many may require you to register with a consumer protection scheme, which you have to pay for.

- **Catalogues**
  Getting your product into a home shopping catalogue is another possibility; the advantage is the catalogue company's much wider reach and its experience of

consumer markets. But their retail price will be several times what they're prepared to give you and they might also want exclusive rights, limiting your ability to sell to anyone else. This may be bearable if the catalogue sells your product well, but a millstone if it doesn't.

- **Consumer direct mail**
  Consumer direct mail will only pay off if your product carries a high value or you get an exceptional response. In the direct mail industry a three per cent response is rated as good. The cost per sale of a one per cent response - and you might not even get that - will easily top £25, comprising 100 stamps, envelopes, print costs and several pence per address if you buy a mailing list. If your product won't sell at a price that pays for the campaign *and* your other overheads *and* gives you a profit, it won't make sense to market it this way.

  As with mail order, response depends heavily on the crafting of the offer you make to potential customers. For example, the more flexible the payment terms the better. Allow payment by cheque, credit card, over the phone (so you can talk to them!); and if the price is high, by instalments. Offer at least 14 days' approval and *always promise an immediate refund if the product is unsuitable for any reason.*

  There are also strict legal restraints on any offer of goods requiring payment in advance, so look thoroughly into the current state of the law before going to print.

  Direct marketing professionals revise and test continuously, slightly changing the offer - down to esoteric details like the angle of the wording on the envelope - to see if orders go up or down, so don't assume your first effort is the best (or worst!) you can do. For know-how read books like Drayton Bird's Commonsense Direct Marketing.

A low cost, low risk way to test consumer direct mail is to forget about addresses and even envelopes. Construct your offer, design and print your mailshot and deliver it door to door, or perhaps pay to have in inserted in a local paper. Better still, design two or three versions for different areas and look out for different levels of response.

- **Business to business direct mail**
  Direct mail makes more sense for a product aimed at businesses, as orders may be fewer in number but larger in value. You can buy business mailing lists - for example from Yellow Pages - based on area, industry or size of company, which makes mailings much more precise. (To minimize wastage on obsolete addresses specify larger companies, as they tend to stay put.) For businesses you can dispense with most of the 'Open Now! Buying Firewood Has Never Been Easier!' hokum that seems de rigeur in consumer direct mail, though you still need to push benefits hard. Your best bet for a high value product may be to invite enquiries rather than attempt a straight sales pitch, as many business customers will want additional information before deciding whether to buy. The more you get to talk to customers, the more you learn what they want and the easier it becomes to sell to them.

- **Leaflets and small ads**
  Most leaflets end up as litter, but few of us throw them away without at least a glance. It's easy and cheap to do your own leafletting, though don't stick them under car screen wipers: that's illegal as well as annoying. Nor need you be limited to local sales, as there are circular distributors everywhere. It may be worth setting up test distributions in different regions to see if there are significant variations in response. (One small business

in Yorkshire offering an innovative photographic service tried this and got by far its best response from Scotland.)

Finally, don't overlook the power of the humble small-ad: we know of one small business that for years got nearly all its work from a regular one-liner in local papers that simply said 'Wrought iron gates from £15. Tel . . . '. With effort you could run something approximating to a national campaign through small-ads, though the logical first step is to test in local papers or a few specialist magazines. As always with advertising, results build with time so you must keep up the effort for at least a few weeks or months.

Summary and checklist

This section summarizes all the key points covered in this book in a format that should make it easy for you to plan your actions and check progress. You don't have to work through tasks strictly in the order listed here, with one vital proviso: *if you don't deal with stages 1, 2 and 3 first and get positive results from all three, you risk wasting a great deal of time and money on an idea that may not be worth pursuing.*

The ▲ symbol indicates danger zones which, in our opinion, you ignore or enter unprepared at your peril.

Chapter 1 : Is your idea original?

- ❍ To count as an invention your idea must be at least partly original and non-obvious. If it isn't, your options are so limited that in most cases it isn't worth carrying on. No company will be interested in a licence. Marketing the product yourself could be an option if you're not infringing anyone else's intellectual property, but marketing an unprotectable idea is extremely risky.
- ▲ Something like nine out of ten 'inventions' aren't original, so before going any further you *must* search for prior art to find whether the inventive steps contained in your idea are already known and recorded.
- ▲ If you discover early on that your idea isn't original, no harm is done. If you carry on *as though* it's original you invite serious financial and legal trouble, possibly including court action by aggrieved patentees or companies with whom you deal.

What you should do

- ❍ Carry out a thorough search of known products, past and present, serving the same need or market. Look for elements similar to those contained in your idea. Tour sales outlets. Read product catalogues, trade journals etc. Talk (cautiously) to people with experience of selling, making or using related products.
- ❍ Carry out a patent search. This may yield vital data about similar ideas which became products *and the many more which didn't, but still count as prior art.*
- ❍ Consult a patent agent for an assessment of your patent search findings if you're not sure whether your idea is sufficiently original to justify going any further.

▲ Don't disclose the detail of your idea to anyone (except patent agents and patent librarians, who in their professional capacity automatically observe confidentiality.)

Cost

Apart from your time and incidental expenses - travel, photocopies etc - £50-200 region for a patent search depending on how many services you use; around £60-100 for a patent agent's assessment of your search findings. (Many patent agents provide free preliminary consultations of around half an hour. If you're organized, a lot can be achieved in that time!)

Risk

None - as long as you're thorough - except possible disappointment.

Important

❍ Carry out both a product search *and* a patent search. One isn't a substitute for the other.

❍ Absence of prior art is not necessarily *lasting* evidence of originality. You must keep up your originality searches for the duration of your project.

❍ If your idea isn't original, it may be possible to improve it and *make* it original. . .

❍ . . . or it may be possible *in some circumstances* to make and market it yourself.

▲ Don't ignore evidence you don't like. (The point of the exercise is to *go looking* for evidence you don't like.)

Chapter 2 : Assessing demand for your idea

❍ You must find out if (a) a worthwhile market exists for your notional product at a price that (b) customers will pay and (c) gives everyone involved a worthwhile profit. A healthy market-price-profit relationship is fundamental to success.

❍ Markets are often elusive and non-obvious. The best market for your product - or the best *initial* market - may be very different from the one you first thought of.

▲ When you find the right market, you'll probably also find that your product's novelty or ingenuity counts for little. For most products, *price* matters most.

What you should do

❍ Identify the problem your idea solves and look at *all* existing ways of tackling it *even if they're very different from your idea. They're all competition.* Is your idea really any better? If so, what's that difference worth?

❍ Identify, research and assess:

- The most profitable market for your idea and - especially if you want to market your own product -
- the easiest, lowest risk market to enter initially. *They may not be the same.*

❍ Find out how well related products sell to give you an idea of market size and potential.

❍ Establish a target selling price and annual sales volume for your product in the market(s) you have identified.

❍ Try to gather reactions to your idea (subject to suitable legal protection) from business people who make, sell or use related products.

❍ Treat informed criticism seriously. You may need to re-think your idea to remove weaknesses. *Some business objections - for example too small a market - may be an early sign that the idea may only succeed if you market it yourself.*

▲ Don't rely only on your own consumer surveys, which although a useful source of market data are often misleading and thus dangerous to use as the *sole* basis of important decision-making.

Cost

Modest and controllable, assuming you don't use professional market researchers (who are usually expensive and geared primarily to helping companies).

Risk

None if you're careful about disclosure. Huge risk from now on if you don't do it.

Important

❍ Keep records of your findings. They may be important in future: to help persuade potential licensing companies or potential backers of your own business, and to keep *you* informed as your project progresses.

❍ Make market research a permanent activity. The more you learn as you go along about the market and its players, the better will be your chances if you later take on an entrepreneurial role.

▲ Don't trust the opinions of friends, relations, neighbours, work colleagues etc. They will lie to you.

Chapter 3 : Proving your idea works

❍ To interest companies or backers you must show that your idea works. Although a rough working prototype will do, the more it looks and performs like a finished product, the better your chances.

❍ Trial batches of product are by far the best persuader (especially if you can prove you've sold some).

▲ Most inventions need at least some redesign to improve their presentation. It helps to get this done before approaching companies, but professional help comes at a price. Options include assigning a stake in your idea. That means sharing profit, but a portion of something is better than the whole of nothing.

What you should do

❍ Prepare a presentation comprising any of these:
- Sample(s) of actual product.
- Full working prototype.
- Rough working prototype plus non-working model to show appearance.
- Dummy packaging.
- Photograph, drawing, artist's impression etc.
- Short, no-frills video.
- Draft leaflet or brochure about your product.

❍ Find out how your prototype is likely to be tested by companies, and what statutory or industry standards it might have to meet.

▲ If you use professionals for prototyping or design, provide a detailed brief as later changes - even apparently minor ones - can be very expensive. Ensure also that they have no legal claim on the product.

- ❍ You may be able to get low-cost help with prototypes and/or design from a university or college.
- ❍ Get quotes from manufacturers for a range of quantities. Provide precise specifications and shop around as prices and terms vary widely. (Data on manufacturing costs is also useful for your market research.)
- ▲ Protect your idea - possibly with a patent application - if your inventive step is likely to be disclosed during prototyping or design.

Cost

Can vary enormously. Think laterally and plan carefully to save money. (For example: could an existing product be adapted cheaply as an acceptable alternative to an expensive custom prototype?)

Risk

Strain on your pocket can be considerable. If you involve anyone else to share the cost, you may lose sole ownership of your idea (but it may still be worth it). To offset disclosure you may have to apply for a patent earlier than you might want and be committed against your will to patent deadlines.

Important

- ❍ *Never underestimate the importance of design. It can transform your prospects.* Even if getting the design right involves giving away a substantial share of your profit, it can be a price well worth paying.
- ❍ If the cost of prototyping and development requires investment beyond your means, think less about spending your own money and more about (a) talking early to suitable companies with a view to licensing or joint venture and/or (b) business start-up strategies including government grant applications.

Chapter 4 : Taking stock

- So far you know that your idea is original, has a potential market and works. You now have to decide whether to go on. The golden rule is: *the potential reward from your idea must be much greater than the cost and risk involved in getting it on to the market.*
- Aiming for a licensing agreement with a company is the safest option for most inventors, but experience suggests that most successful inventors get results - which can include licensing agreements - only when they assume an entrepreneurial role. That doesn't mean giving up an existing job; it's fairly easy to run a small business as a sideline with minimal overheads and relatively few risks.

What you should do

- Spend lots of time thinking, re-thinking and planning.

Risk

None while you're thinking. Some risk is inevitable from now on, but the more planning you do, the less risk you run.

Important

- From now on you need to concentrate on *avoiding mistakes*, as any you do make could be expensive.

Chapter 5 : Getting help

❍ Developing a product demands a range of skills and resources that few individuals possess, so from now on *get help.*

What you should do

❍ Look for sources of help, advice, referrals etc on a wide range of business and innovation topics - for example Business Links, innovation centres, universities, chambers of commerce, local councils.

Cost

There should be little or no direct cost, but some forms of help may only be available if you're prepared to share some of your profits or set up a business.

Risk

Some risk of disclosure, so make sure your legal protection is adequate for this stage.

Important

▲ Beware of consultants, invention agencies, 'product development' companies and others offering to make you rich. Some are genuine but expensive; many simply want large sums of money off you for doing (usually) little or nothing.

Chapter 6 : Intellectual property

- If your idea has commercial prospects, it's essential to protect it legally so that you can make better progress by being able to disclose it to others in relative safety, and have some defence against anyone who tries to profit from your idea without first entering into an agreement with you.
- If you can afford it, or if the income potential of your idea is considerable, use a patent agent from the outset. Brief but useful initial consultations are often free.

What you should do

- Study the pros and cons of the forms of protection available (confidentiality, copyright, design right, design registration, trade mark, patent).
- Get the best single or combined protection *appropriate to your idea and its income potential.* If that is low, it isn't worth spending much on protection - which may rule out a full patent.
- Make sure you also protect every variation of your idea you can think of, so that your intellectual property can't easily be circumvented by someone changing details or seeing your idea and thinking of an improvement.
- If a patent is what you think you want, act only when you understand what's involved as it's a complex area.
- ▲ *Don't rush to patent.* Filing a patent application too early is a common mistake that lands many inventors in trouble later. File only when detailed disclosure becomes unavoidable - for example when a company wants to see your idea - OR be prepared to let the application lapse and re-file with loss of priority.

Cost

Can range from free (confidentiality, copyright and design right) to four- or five-figure expensive if you patent. Costs can be minimized if you plan your filing strategy carefully, or find a company willing to pay the full patenting costs which become due 12 months later.

Risk

No form of protection is risk free. There is no risk getting copyright for example, but its protection may be inadequate. There are high risks associated with the cost of getting a patent but potentially greater risks if you don't have one. *All risks are reduced if you know what you're doing, and why.*

Important

❍ For all officially registrable protection use a patent agent from the start if you can afford it, or from the first sign that your idea is a winner. *Intellectual property is what you're selling to companies or building your own business round, so it needs to be as strong as possible.*

❍ Don't lose sight of the usefulness of other forms of protection as alternatives or additions to patents. A trade mark, for example, could ultimately be your most valuable asset.

❍ Make all your decisions on patenting dependent on (a) your search results and (b) funds available.

▲ Don't assume a patent will make you rich. That's not what they're for, and most patents are never taken up commercially.

▲ Don't assume a patent (or any other form of protection) will stop people stealing your idea. All it does is put you in a stronger position if you ever get them into court. Even then there's no guarantee you'll win.

Chapter 7 : Benefits of licensing

- Few inventors have all the abilities or resources needed to exploit their ideas commercially. Licensing the idea to a company is for most inventors the best chance to profit from their idea at the lowest personal risk.
- Licensing in ideas benefits companies too, as few can now afford their own R&D. In general, companies are increasingly willing to look outside for new ideas.
- Even if you prefer to start your own business, licensing your idea to other companies can be an effective way to widen your markets, increase your profits or limit your risk.

What you should do

- If you decide that the licensing route is the one to follow, make sure that absolutely everything of potential value is the subject of a licence. Otherwise you may be persuaded to omit as a 'minor detail' an element of your intellectual property - for example a trade mark - that could turn out to be enormously valuable later.

Important

- Although licensing offers the lowest personal risk to most inventors, it doesn't necessarily offer the best prospects of getting the product to market. That may lie in starting your own business (Chapters 13 onwards).
- If there is more than one owner of an idea, all must agree to the granting of a licence. This is frequently a source of problems.

Chapter 8 : Selecting companies to approach

▲ Chose companies with care. There are drawbacks to approaching very large companies and - for different reasons - very small companies.

❍ In general you need to look for companies of *the right size and capabilities* to whom you can offer either *larger market share* or a *strengthened product range.* Your ideal company is likely to be in the small to medium-sized sector.

❍ The fewer companies there are to approach, the better your presentation has to be as the risk of 100 per cent rejection is higher.

What you should do

❍ Based on your estimate of potential sales volume and profitability, assess whether your product is best suited to a large or a smaller company.

❍ Find out how companies in your target market primarily get their ideas. (Many may only consider ideas from other companies or from their own R&D.)

❍ Compile a list of 'possibles' from your market research and/or from sources such as the Kompass directory.

❍ If you can ask without disclosure, chambers of commerce or other business advice agencies may be able to give you useful local leads.

▲ Publicity about your invention may generate interest and coax out companies you'd never have found. *You must however be adequately protected; pre-protection publicity can be deadly.*

❍ You may need to identify at least two companies - one

to make and one or more to market the product. *This could be the start of an entrepreneurial role that leads you away from licensing and towards business start-up.*

❍ Review your intellectual property protection (including your confidentiality agreement). Now that you're ready to go semi-public, is it strong enough?

Cost

Insignificant.

Risk

Mainly that you end up wasting time and effort on the wrong companies.

Important

❍ Once you start approaching firms you're racing against time, particularly if you've applied for a patent, so identify target companies with as much care and precision as possible.

▲ It can be a mistake - for several reasons - to target only market leaders. For the average new product, smaller firms may be a safer bet.

Chapter 9 : The initial approach

- ❍ To get companies to take serious notice of you at all, your approach needs to be competent and professional.

What you should do

- ❍ Initially, send a brief business letter and summary of the idea to marketing rather than technical managers.
- ▲ Try to get a confidentiality agreement signed before any meeting (though many companies will refuse).
- ❍ For meetings, prepare an 'act' that conveys the key benefits of your idea in 10-15 minutes, and a dossier of back-up information to help answer questions.
- ❍ Write a record of your meeting - names, job titles, reactions, actions promised etc - as soon as you leave.
- ▲ Don't call yourself an inventor.
- ▲ Don't reveal anything about your intellectual property.

Cost

Insignificant.

Risk

Substantial. This is it: you're telling companies about your idea. Most you can trust, some you can't. And even the interested ones may drag their feet while your patent application clock ticks furiously.

Important

- ❍ Learn from mistakes or setbacks.
- ▲ Confirm every move in writing and keep copies of all correspondence. It prevents misunderstanding and protects you against possible broken faith later.

Chapter 10 : Assessment by companies

- ❍ Interested companies may want to keep your prototype for weeks of assessment, while you need it available to show other companies, especially if patenting deadlines are rushing to meet you. How do you stay in control?

What you should do

- ❍ Only release your prototype subject to a formal loan agreement with a specified end-date.
- ❍ Find out what the company will do to your prototype, and how well they'll look after it.
- ▲ Don't loan your prototype for long without some form of payment related to the potential value of the product; and the more the company wants your prototype on its own terms, the more they should pay. Payment terms must be written into the loan contract.

Important

- ❍ Remember: your prototype is your property. You have every right to keep it under your full control, even when it's on loan to a company.
- ▲ *It's* vital *to receive adequate and guaranteed payment for a protracted or restrictive loan period.*
- ❍ Payment in instalments is usually more acceptable to companies than a lump sum. But make it clear in your contract that if a payment fails to materialize, any agreement is instantly void.
- ❍ Payment should also cover upkeep costs, especially patenting. A patent agent can help to make sure the company does everything on time and as agreed.

Chapter 11 : Reaching agreement

❍ Negotiating a licensing agreement with a company is easier if you can prevent conflict. *Often the biggest problem is the inventor's greed or inflexibility.*

❍ There are normally two stages of negotiation: *heads of agreement* in which you agree broad terms, followed by *full agreement* which is strictly for legal professionals.

What you should do

❍ First work out the broad figures, terms and conditions you want. *They must be commercially realistic.*

▲ Enlist professional help if the agreement will be complex - for example, covering overseas sales by associate companies - or if the product has high income potential.

▲ Don't try to undo deals after heads of agreement stage.

Cost

Fees for legal and professional services.

Risk

Varies with your attitude, ability and preparation - and the expertise of any professional negotiating help!

Important

❍ Remember that *the object of negotiation is not to win but to reach agreement. . .*

❍ . . .but *always walk away rather than accept a bad deal.*

▲ Once you've reached agreement, honour it even if you feel (or are advised) that you could do better. You risk wrecking the whole deal by attempting to change the score after the whistle.

Chapter 12 : Working out royalties

- ❍ The royalty you deserve should be based primarily on the value of your product, though your contribution to its development may also be a significant factor.
- ❍ Royalties are usually expressed as a percentage of net sales price, but this is no measure of *value* and thus no indication of the royalty percentage you should get.
- ❍ A better indicator of value is gross profit per unit and probable market size. The bigger the potential gross profit, the better your prospects of a high royalty.

What you should do

- ❍ Align your expectations with reality by averaging out three variables: your contribution to the product, the product's likely profitability and its likely sales volume.
- ❍ Estimate the product's likely *gross profit per unit* (selling price minus manufacturing cost) and *probable market size*.
- ❍ For most products the best royalty bid is likely to be for 10-25 per cent of gross profit per unit.
- ❍ Demonstrate a willingness to be flexible, for example by accepting or suggesting a sliding scale of royalties.
- ▲ *Don't demand a large lump-sum advance payment as you're unlikely to get it.* If production is some way off, ask for a guaranteed minimum income until then, perhaps to be deducted from royalties.
- ▲ *If offered a fixed sum instead of royalties, examine the offer carefully.* The company is gambling that it can buy you out relatively cheaply, but you could end up the winner if sales don't take off as expected.

- ❍ Alternatively: accept a fixed sum but only on condition that you get more if sales exceed a certain level.

Important

- ❍ Your financial expectations must be realistic or agreement may be impossible.
- ❍ Actual income potential matters more than the size of the royalty percentage. A tiny percentage of a product bought in millions can make you a lot richer than a large percentage of a poor seller.
- ▲ *Never agree to royalties based on profit alone*; companies can too easily 'prove' that they haven't made a profit.
- ❍ If your own bottom line and company's final offer are too far apart, don't be afraid to pull out and look for better prospects elsewhere.

Chapter 13 : Starting your own business

- If you can't get a licensing deal with any company, it may be worth considering setting up your own business to get your product to market.
- This needn't mean abandoning your hunt for a licensing deal. *You need only operate a business for as long as it takes to find out if your product sells or not.* If it does, you can go back to companies later with proof of sales.
- It's often possible to run this kind of business - which is effectively in-depth market research - in spare time.

What you should do

- Consider the pre-conditions:
  - Grounds to believe your product will sell.
  - A product that doesn't need levels of finance no one will give you.
  - A clear idea of your motivation and goals.
- Limit your start-up costs, for example by working from home and subcontracting manufacture.
- Make sure you stay in day-by-day control.
- As far as possible make your costs dependent on sales.
- Be wary of banks.
- Choose your customers with care.

Important

- In order to survive, your overriding priority should always be to *limit your risk.* As one multi-millionaire entrepreneur says: 'You can't hope to get it right if you don't first reduce your chances of getting it wrong'.

Chapter 14 : Joint venture

- ❍ *As long as you have relevant expertise and behave professionally* a joint venture with a company can be an excellent way to develop your product, with mutual benefits.
- ❍ If you link up with a small company, the most realistic aim may be to develop and test-market the product with a view to licensing to a larger company.

What you should do

- ❍ Satisfy the potential partner company that your idea is sound - and that you are too!
- ❍ Discuss and agree objectives before starting the project. Can you meet the company's requirements? Are deadlines and budgets realistic? etc.
- ▲ *Get your agreement in writing* and have it drafted or checked by your solicitor and/or patent agent. Make sure it covers all areas that could be a problem later - for example who owns improvements to the product.

Cost

Low, or you wouldn't be doing it.

Risk

Mainly that the project founders because one of you fails to deliver.

Important

- ❍ A joint venture may be the only way you'll get your product to market, so look for opportunities and treat any ensuing project as a serious business enterprise.

Chapter 15 : Business plan

- ❍ A business plan is vital for most new enterprises; more so for innovation ventures, as the greater number of 'unknowns' makes it even harder to attract backing.
- ❍ A business plan reduces early risk by enabling you or others to spot potential problems and deal with them.

What you should do

- ❍ Describe your business plans plainly and clearly under separate headings: the business, the product, the market, the human resources, future prospects etc.
- ❍ Prepare a financial plan justifying the need for investment, and indicating how investors can pull out with a fat profit after three to five years.
- ❍ Include 'What if?' versions of your cash flow forecast to deal with some of the inevitable uncertainties.

Important

- ❍ Don't make the mistake of thinking that only other people need your business plan. It's primarily a tool to reveal truths about your business to *you*, even though you may use it to attract support from others.
- ❍ Many investors look primarily at one thing: the quality of management. If you're found wanting, they may not want to invest no matter how good the product and its prospects.
- ▲ Present your proposed business in its best light but don't massage figures or fictionalize your business plan. Such attempts will be detected; in any case your plan is primarily to help you, so why fool yourself?

Chapter 16 : Raising finance

❍ Early-stage funding is hard to get. Basic sources are:
- Personal finance: family, friends or 'business angels'.
- Business partners, perhaps via a joint venture.
- Public funds: government or local authority grants.
- Venture capital (though unlikely for inexperienced start-ups or for requirements below £250,000).
- Publicity: a 'wild card' that can attract support from unexpected sources.

What you should do

❍ The lower the risk to investors, the better your chances; so you must convince them that your business aims are achievable and you'll spend their money wisely. A key vehicle for this is your business and financial plan.

❍ Try to get advance orders *even if you haven't yet got any product to deliver*; it reduces the perceived risk of backing an untried product.

❍ Examine whether you need significant external funding at all. If you can, adopt a strategy that requires a relatively small amount of funding to *sell* your product rather than a much larger amount to *manufacture* it.

Important

❍ Don't expect any help from banks unless you've got firm orders or a healthy business track record.

❍ Most investors (other than perhaps family and friends) will look primarily at the soundness of the *management* of your proposed enterprise.

▲ Beware giving away too much control of your business and/or product in return for investment.

Chapter 17 : Low-cost marketing

- Getting your marketing right is vital; it's at least as important as getting your product right.
- For a new product, marketing involves two phases: informing potential customers that your product exists, then (later) analysing sales patterns to make your marketing more effective.
- Unless you're adequately funded you'll have to do your own initial marketing; cost usually rules out marketing professionals and/or media advertising.

What you should do

- Learn about marketing (read, or look for local short courses).
- Devise and activate an appropriate marketing strategy before you start trading.
- Learn how to use press releases to get free publicity for your product and business.
- Prepare product literature to mail out. Entry level is a standard letter, but watch cost and other factors if you need a printed leaflet or brochure.
- Monitor the source of all enquiries so you can gradually improve your marketing.

Important

- *Always* focus on the benefits of your product.
- Your message and the way you convey it must be appropriate to the market.

Chapter 18 : Selling

- ❍ If you're running your business on a shoe-string your selling strategy should be based on (a) minimizing overheads and (b) not giving away too much profit to anyone else except in return for improved performance.
- ❍ Your best options may include mail order, direct mail, catalogues, leaflets and small ads.

What you should do

- ❍ Consider the type of selling that best suits your product, its market and your budget.
- ▲ Choose a *controllable* option so that if it isn't working you can stop or change it immediately.
- ▲ If you intend to sell by mail, make sure you comply with relevant consumer legislation and industry regulation.

Important

- ▲ Whatever option you choose, study the probable *cost per sale* carefully or the cost of your sales effort could exceed profit.

Useful addresses

To the uninitiated, compiling a short list of contacts might seem a piece of cake. In practice it's remarkably difficult, as many organizations change their names and phone numbers with fiendish regularity and become hard to trace. Although we've done our best to make the following information up-to-date, it's inevitable that some details will soon be wrong, so make your own checks before taking any action.

It's also important to stress that we've aimed only to provide a 'starter pack' of contacts. There are many more public sector, academic and private sector organizations which may be able to help with specifics. Most should in theory be traceable though the general contacts in Sections 1-3.

1 Innovation and enterprise agencies

First ports of call where individuals should get a professional hearing in confidence and a reasonable amount of free advice, or referral to a more specific source of help.

- Ogwr Partnership Trust Enterprise Centre Bryn Road Tondu BRIDGEND CF32 9BS (01656) 724414
- BRAVE Enterprise Agency 2 Upper York Street BRISTOL BS2 8QN (0117) 927 2222
- Cornwall Innovation Centre 28 Chapel Street CAMBORNE TR14 8EL (01209) 612670
- North Derbyshire Enterprise Agency Enterprise House 123 Saltergate CHESTERFIELD S40 1NH (01246) 207379
- Innovation North William Street GATESHEAD NE10 0JP (0191) 495 0066

- North East Innovation Centre Neilson Road GATESHEAD NE10 0EW (0191) 490 1222
- Glasgow Opportunities 7 West George Street GLASGOW G2 1BQ (0141) 221 0955
- Merseyside Innovation Centre 131 Mount Pleasant LIVERPOOL L3 5TF (0151) 708 0123
- The Ulster Business School The University of Ulster Jordonstown Shore Road NEWTON ABBEY BT37 0QB (01232) 365060
- Enterprise Plymouth Somerset Place PLYMOUTH PL3 4BB (01752) 569211
- SEHEA Regional Business Centre Baltic House Kingston Crescent PORTSMOUTH PO2 8QL (01705) 666622
- Restormel Local Enterprise Trust Par Moor Road ST AUSTELL PL25 3RF (01276) 813079
- SCEPTRE Sheffield Hallam University City Campus SHEFFIELD S1 1WB (0114) 225 3450
- Sandwell Enterpise Business Advice Centre Victoria Street WEST BROMWICH B70 8ET (0121) 500 5412

2 Innovation and business development bodies

All these are members of the EU's European Business Network.

- Barnsley BIC Innovation Way BARNSLEY S75 1JL (01226) 249590
- Birmingham Technology Ltd Aston Science Park Love Lane BIRMINGHAM B7 4BJ (0121) 359 0981
- Blackburn Technology Management Centre Challenge Way Greenbank Technology Park BLACKBURN BB1 5QB (01254) 692692
- St John's Innovation Centre Ltd Cowley Road CAMBRIDGE CB4 4WS (01223) 420252
- Innovation Wales BIC (SEWBIC) Cardiff Business Technology Centre Sengennydd Road CARDIFF CF2 4AY (01222) 372311
- Scottish Innovation Templeton Business Centre 62 Templeton Street GLASGOW G40 1DA (0141) 554 5995
- Pronovus Howitt Building Lenton Boulevard NOTTINGHAM NG7 2BG (0115) 952 9320

- Innovation Centre NORIBIC 9 Shipquay Street LONDONDERRY BT48 6DJ (01504) 264242
- Greater Manchester BIC Windmill Lane Denton MANCHESTER M34 3QS (0161) 337 8648
- Staffordshire & Black Country BIC Staffordshire Technology Park Beaconside STAFFORD ST18 0AR (01785) 226598
- Sunderland BIC Sunderland Enterprise Park Wearfield SUNDERLAND SR5 2TA (0191) 5160160

3 Business Links, Business Shops etc

A network of some 200 local points of access to all the information, advice and support needed by businesses in areas including innovation, design, finance and start-up. In England, to find your nearest Business Link either phone 0800 500 200 or contact one of these regional Government Offices (GOs):

- GO-West Midlands 77 Paradise Circus Queensway BIRMINGHAM B1 2D (0121) 212 5118
- GO-Eastern Region Building A Westbrook Centre Milton Road CAMBRIDGE CA4 1YG (01223) 461939
- GO-South East Bridge House 1 Walnut Tree Close GUILDFORD GU1 4GA (01483) 882547
- GO-Yorkshire & Humberside 25 Queen Street LEEDS LS1 2TW (0113) 280 0600
- GO-Merseyside Graeme House Derby Square LIVERPOOL L2 7UP (0151) 224 6306
- GO-London Riverwalk House 157-161 Millbank LONDON SW1P 4RR (0171) 217 3456
- GO-North West Sunley Tower Piccadilly Plaza MANCHESTER M1 4BA (0161) 952 4122
- GO-North East Stanegate House Groat Market NEWCASTLE UPON TYNE NE1 1YN (0191) 201 3300
- GO-East Midlands The Belgrave Centre Stanley Place Talbot Street NOTTINGHAM NG1 5GG (0115) 971 9971
- GO-South West (Devon & Cornwall) Phoenix House Notte Street PLYMOUTH PL1 2HF (01752) 221891

In Scotland a similar system of Business Shops is run by Scottish Enterprise and the Local Enterprise Companies. Find your nearest one by ringing 0800 787878 or by contacting:

- The Scottish Office Education & Industry Department Meridian Court Cadogan Street GLASGOW G2 6AT (0141) 248 2855

Similarly in Wales, find local help from Business Connect . Ring (0345) 969798 or contact:

- The Welsh Office Industry & Training Department Cathays Park CARDIFF CF1 3NQ (01222) 825111

4 The Patent Office

- Central Enquiry Unit The Patent Office Cardiff Road NEWPORT NP9 1RH (0645) 500 505
  Contact the CEU for specific enquiries on patents, designs, trade and service marks, copyright.
- Search & Advisory Service (01633) 811010
  Carries out patent and trade/service mark searches at commercial rates.

5 Patent Libraries

- Patents Section Central Library Belfast Public Libraries Royal Avenue BELFAST BT1 1EA (01232) 243233
- Patent Department Central Library Chamberlain Square BIRMINGHAM B3 3HQ (0121) 235 4537
- Business Users' Service Mitchell Library North Street GLASGOW G3 7DN (0141) 287 2905
- Patents Information Unit. Leeds Public Libraries 32 York Road LEEDS LS9 8TD (0113) 214 3347
- Central Library William Brown Street LIVERPOOL L3 8EW (0151) 225 5440/2
- Science Reference & Information Services British Library 25 Southampton Buildings Chancery Lane LONDON WC2A 1AW (0171) 412 7919/20
- Patent Advice Centre Central Library Princess Square NEWCASTLE UPON TYNE NE99 1DX (0191) 232 4601
- Business & Technology Library Central Library Surrey Street SHEFFIELD S1 1XZ (0114) 273 4742

6 Patent Information Centres

Hold patent abstracts, abridgements and guidance material only.

- Business & Technical Department Central Library Rosemount Viaduct ABERDEEN AB25 1GW (01224) 634622
- Commercial Library Central Library College Green BRISTOL BS1 5TL (0117) 929 9148
- Lanchester Library Coventry University Much Park Street COVENTRY CV1 2HF (01203) 838167
- Technical Library Central Library St Peter's Square MANCHESTER M2 5PD (0161) 234 1987
- Reference Library Central Library Drake Circus PLYMOUTH PL4 8AL (01752) 385906
- Central Library Guildhall Square PORTSMOUTH PO1 2DX (01705) 819311

7 Patent & trade mark agents

Practices are listed in Yellow Pages, but for a full list and literature contact:

- Chartered Institute of Patent Agents (CIPA) Staple Inn Buildings High Holborn LONDON WC1V 7PZ (0171) 405 9450

CIPA runs free clinics (see below) in London, Birmingham, Liverpool, East Anglia and Yorkshire plus a scheme where patent agents provide a free initial consultation. As well as free booklets on patents, design and trade marks, it can provide speakers on intellectual property issues for groups.

8 Patent clinics

CIPA runs these free clinics:

- Patents & Technology Section Birmingham Central Library Chamberlain Square BIRMINGHAM B3 3HQ. Every Wednesday evening. Appointment necessary: contact Ted Hunt on (0121) 235 4537.
- EAST ANGLIA Every 4-6 weeks or so at either Ipswich & Suffolk Chamber of Commerce, Suffolk Enterprise Centre, Russell Road, Ipswich IP1 2DE or Colchester Institute, Sheepen Road, Colchester CO1 1DA. For an appointment ring Julie Barrett-Major on (01206) 571187.

- Science & Technology Library Central Library William Brown Street LIVERPOOL L3 8EW. Alternate Tuesday evenings. Appointment necessary: contact David Wilkinson on (0151) 225 5442.
- LONDON The Chartered Institute of Patent Agents (address/phone as above). Every Tuesday evening - appointment necessary. Contact Michele Tinsley.
- YORKSHIRE Monthly patent clinics are held at these centres:
  Bradford Business & Innovation Centre
  Batley Business & Technology Centre
  Business Link Wakefield & District, Castleford Office
  Business Link Leeds Office.
  Ring Jonathan Nott on (01274) 754169/754262 for details.
- Leeds Patent Information Unit (details above) also provides its own demonstrations of patent searching.

9 Other professional help

- Institute of Trade Mark Agents Canterbury House 2-6 Sydenham Road CROYDON CR0 9XE (0181) 686 2052
- Register of Trade Mark Agents Address as above
- Licensing Executives Society Ltd (LES) Ms Renate Siebrasse c/o MEDTAP International Inc 27 Gilbert Street LONDON W1Y 1RL (0171) 290 9400
- The Law Society P O Box 61 LONDON NW1 7QS (0171) 405 9075

  Contact the Law Society for a list of participating professionals in a scheme called Lawyers for Your Business, which provides a free initial consultation to discuss your business affairs.

10 Information for market and product research

- Your local reference or university library
  Many public libraries include departments or separate units specializing in commercial information, increasingly with on-line facilities. As a member of the public you can usually use university libraries, though you may need to make special arrangements to use some facilities or services.
- The British Library
  Source of all UK companies information including annual reports, market research reports and journals, directories, trade, business and product literature.

- The British Library Business Information Service 25 Southampton Buildings LONDON WC2A 1AW (0171) 323 7454 for quick enquires; (0171) 323 7979 for fee-based search and research service.
- Companies House (England and Wales) Crown Way CARDIFF CF4 3UZ (01222) 388588
- Companies House (Scotland) 37 Castle Terrace EDINBURGH EH1 2EB (0131) 535 5800
  Information including annual accounts on all UK registered companies.
- Export Market Information Centre Department of Trade & Industry Ashdown House 123 Victoria Street LONDON SW1E 6RB
  (0171) 215 5444/5
  Major UK source of home and international market research information. Free enquiry service plus photocopying, database searching, market research, trade directories.
- Market Research Society 15 Northburgh Street LONDON EC1V 0AH (0171) 490 4911
  Information and professional contacts. Publishes a free periodical called Survey and an Organisation Book listing members and their areas of specialist expertise.
- British Standards Institution 389 Chiswick High Road LONDON W4 4AL (0181) 996 9000
  UK national body for setting product safety and quality standards. Full information service and testing service for new products.

11 Independent advisory bodies

- Institute of Patentees & Inventors Suite 505a Triumph House 189 Regent Street LONDON W1R 7WF (0171) 434 1818
- Intellectual Property Development Association 72A Bedford Place SOUTHAMPTON SO15 2DS (01703) 570101
- Local Enterprise Agencies
  For details of over 300 local agencies contact Business in the Community 44 Baker Street LONDON W1M 1DH (0171) 224 1600
- London Chamber of Commerce & Industry 33 Queen Street LONDON EC4R 1AP (0171) 248 4444
- UK Science Parks Association Business & Innovation Centre Aston Science Park Love Lane BIRMINGHAM B7 4BJ (0121) 359 9081
  Helps stimulate development of high technology businesses by providing start-up premises linked to universities, institutes and research centres.

- Regional Technology Centres National contact point (0191) 516 4400
  Help transfer technology from research into manufacture.
- Innovation Relay Centres Contact point (0191) 516 4402
  Provide advice on EU funding and programmes.
- Chartered Institute of Marketing Moor Hall Cookham MAIDENHEAD SL6 9QH
  Register of marketing consultants. Runs the Marketing Initiative scheme, part of DTI's Enterprise Initiative.

12 Funding

Contacts in other sections may also be able to advise or assist, but in general don't expect financial help to be easy to get. A sound business plan is always essential.

- British Technology Group Ltd 101 Newington Causeway LONDON SE1 6BU (0171) 403 6666
  For new scientific and engineering products. Can also help with licensing.
- British Venture Capital Association Essex House 12-13 Essex Street LONDON WC2R 3AA Tel (0171) 240 3846 Fax (0171) 240 3849
  Helps put those wanting venture and seed capital in touch with those who provide it. Among its publications for entrepreneurs is a free directory Sources of Business Angel Capital. Business angels are individuals willing to make the smaller investments - typically £10,000-100,000 - that many innovators need but usually can't get from large institutional investors. A sound business and financial plan remains essential though.
- 3i plc 91 Waterloo Road LONDON SE1 8XP (0171) 928 3131
  Seed capital for innovative projects, though tends to deal with existing companies rather than individuals.
- LINC (Local Investment Networking Company) c/o General Manager LINC London Enterprise Agency 4 Snow Hill LONDON EC1A 2BS (0171) 332 0877
  Nationwide introduction service for investors and businesses seeking growth and start-up capital.

13 Government and EU funding

Several schemes are available to help with R&D and consultancy costs. Apart from the SMART Award (Section 15) none is really appropriate for individuals, though some are targeted at smaller businesses and so may be of use to a company wanting to take up your idea. Some also involve links with academic institutions. Schemes come and go, so contact a Business Link or Government Office (Section 3) for current information and advice on which, if any, apply to you.

- Finance from Europe
  A booklet co-produced by NatWest and available from the Central Office of Information, giving a wealth of information about EU support schemes for research and development.

14 Banks

Banks don't normally provide development capital, but they may back a promising new business if your product is up and running. All banks listen, but the bigger the branch, the less you may have to shout. Bear in mind that bank managers are generally not technology specialists, and can only base lending judgments on sound business and financial plans.

- NatWest Innovation & Growth Unit (0171) 454 2847
  Has specialist Technology Managers in various branches in the UK.

15 Competitions

Innovation competitions where you stand to win money and/or further support plus credibility and, as long as your idea is adequately protected, valuable publicity. There may be others, but only enter if they are backed by reputable bodies.

- SMART Awards (Small Firms Merit Award for Research and Technology)
  Contact via a Business Link
  A competition for individuals or firms of under 50 employees with innovative technological ideas which are stalled through lack of funds. Stage 1 offers up to £45,000 towards a feasibility study; Stage 2 offers up to about £120,000 toward development of a pre-production prototype.
- Prince of Wales Award for Innovation Business in the Community
  44 Baker Street LONDON W1M 1DH (0171) 224 1600
  Open to anyone attempting to create new business based on a British

invention or new idea. Finalists appear on a special edition of BBC TV's Tomorrow's World. Winners get help in reaching production and can use the Award emblem for five years.

- Some Training and Enterprise Councils (TECs) run or support regional innovation award schemes.

16 Europe

The EU provides a wide range of support for innovation, especially in new and emerging technologies. It's hard to enter the EU arena alone as most schemes are geared to companies and academic institutions, but it's worth trying to get an appropriate 'team' together if your idea has international potential. European Community Offices are in theory founts of information about all aspects of the EU, though in practice it may be better to make initial or general enquiries at your nearest Business Link.

- Commission of the European Communities Windsor House 9/15 Bedford Street BELFAST BT2 7EG (01232) 240708
- Commission of the European Communities 4 Cathedral Road CARDIFF CF1 9SG (01222) 371631
- Commission of the European Communities Jean Monnet Centre 39 Molesworth Street DUBLIN 2 (00 353) 166 25113
- Commission of the European Communities Alva Street EDINBURGH EH2 4PH (0131) 225 2058
- Commission of the European Communities Jean Monnet House 8 Storey's Gate LONDON SW1P 3AT (0171) 973 1992